" La carte est le document de base indispensable pour la Géographie, et ce ne sont pas des géographes qui la dressent."

CAMILLE VALLAUX, *Les Sciences Géographiques*

AN
INTRODUCTION TO THE
STUDY OF MAP
PROJECTIONS

BY

J. A. STEERS, M.A.

FELLOW AND DEAN OF ST. CATHARINE'S COLLEGE, UNIVERSITY
LECTURER IN GEOGRAPHY

WITH A FOREWORD BY
F. DEBENHAM, M.A., O.B.E.

FELLOW OF GONVILLE AND CAIUS COLLEGE, AND PROFESSOR
OF GEOGRAPHY IN THE UNIVERSITY OF CAMBRIDGE

THIRD EDITION, REVISED AND ENLARGED

UNIVERSITY OF LONDON PRESS, Ltd.
10 & 11 WARWICK LANE, LONDON, E.C.4
1933

FIRST PRINTED . . . *January* 1927
SECOND EDITION . . . *July* 1929
THIRD EDITION . . . *April* 1933

Printed in Great Britain for the UNIVERSITY OF LONDON PRESS, LTD.,
by HAZELL, WATSON AND VINEY, LTD., London and Aylesbury.

FOREWORD

THE subject of Map Projections has been receiving increased attention of late years from students of Geography, and a small group of books has kept pace with that interest. In a great measure the attention now given is due to the appearance, many years ago, of articles and books on the subject by Colonel Sir Charles Close and Mr. A. R. Hinks, which remain the standard works in English.

As successor to the latter in the Lectureship in Cartography at this University I have had ample evidence both of the need for the study of Projections and of the difficulties presented by it to the non-mathematical student.

That there is a wide gulf fixed between the simple mathematics of projections and the understanding of one type of student is shown by the remark of one such. At the end of a course of lectures on Projections he said to me : " I was very interested in your lectures and found these mathematical methods very pretty, but as a matter of fact I avoid all that sort of thing by simply copying from a globe when I want a true map."

Even allowing for the faulty presentation of the subject of which I had obviously been guilty, the remark does, nevertheless, represent the attitude of quite a considerable proportion of Geography students. They are apt to consider Projections as a side-issue, an unnecessary

v

excursion into the byways of mathematical geography, and they blandly continue to commit heinous crimes in the name of cartography by measuring areas on a Mercator projection or taking bearings from a Bonne.

To such people the excellent book on Map Projections by Mr. Hinks becomes a tribulation, just as commencing Latin translation with Horace would be. There are at least two Cæsars as alternatives, the works of Mr. Morrison and Dr. Garnett, but neither of these quite meets the case of students in Geography at a university who hope to go on to their Horace later.

It was for that reason that when Mr. Steers came to me a year or so ago, full of his hobby, inquiring whether there was room for another edition of Cæsar, I commended the plan and awaited the result with interest.

To the class of student referred to above in somewhat scathing terms I must add another class, those who, while just as troubled by mathematics as the others, realise the necessity for projections and find that when grasped boldly the subject has few stings and can give full satisfaction to the average geographer without recourse to anything beyond elementary trigonometry. Indeed, if the student commencing the subject would but regard it with the same attitude as that with which he sits down to a cross-word puzzle or a pictorial maze the Cæsar stage would very soon be passed.

It is, I imagine, to encourage the latter class and to cajole the former class that Mr. Steers has written this book, and, judging from its proof-form, I believe he has produced the thing required. To the mathematician it will carry but small appeal, and may be criticised for some of its approximations, but to the general student it may well become a pleasant path, satisfying by the way and leading if necessary to the advanced works of Hinks and Germain and Young.

May I add a hint or two for the benefit of beginners ? I am convinced that the only way to study projections with any real satisfaction is to construct them oneself, and the problem gains in perspective if one imagines one is doing exactly what our former student said he did, copying from a globe. We choose our scale—which should be small if we are to avoid trouble with curves of large radius—and visualise an earth of that scale, that is, a globe. Given its radius, we have all we want in the way of fundamental measurement, from which, following the examples given in this book, a short list of distances on paper is compiled, and the rest is comparatively simple work with ruler, protractor, and compass. Complete understanding and satisfaction comes when over the finished graticule the country itself is drawn in. A new light on cartography is apt to dawn upon the beginner when he realises that it is in just such a way that the draughtsmen of the great Claudius Ptolemæus were set to work to draw their maps 1,400 years ago, and the draughtsmen of Bartholomew to-day are producing the atlases which are the fundamental instrument of the geographer.

A few such exercises, pursued to the end, will do more to convince the student of the meaning and limitations of scale, of the necessity for projections, and finally of their essential simplicity in most cases, than the diligent reading of any number of books.

In the course of many conferences with Mr. Steers over the plan of this book we have agreed generally on the methods of presentation, so that I feel I should share in any criticisms that may be aimed at it, yet, since

FOREWORD

I have taken no part in the actual production, I can claim no share of what eulogies it may earn. I can, therefore, commend the book without any hesitation to those who may be embarking upon a reputedly knotty subject, as one which not only explains the knots, but to a great extent shows that they hardly exist.

F. DEBENHAM.

GONVILLE AND CAIUS COLLEGE,
CAMBRIDGE.

PREFACE TO THE THIRD EDITION

This edition differs from the second in several respects.

(1) A few minor alterations have been made in the text.

(2) The appendix on Conical Projections has now been made an integral part of the chapters dealing with these projections. The alternative construction of the Simple Conic with Two Standard Parallels now comes in the first part of the book, and the details of the Conical Equal Area with one Standard Parallel and Albers' Projection are included in Part II in the appropriate chapter. The short note on Mercator's Projection, which formed the second appendix of the earlier edition, is added as a note to the chapter on Mercator. These changes have been made to balance the book: there is otherwise always a danger of making the appendices equivalent to a third part.

(3) Two new chapters (IX and XII) have been added. The first deals with the Parabolic and similar projections, the second gives in very brief outline a few notes on recent and unusual projections. No mathematical detail is given in this chapter. The construction of the graticules is not easy, and any attempt to give details would be out of place in such a volume as this. Nevertheless, the student should be familiar with the nature of these projections, and it is for this reason the chapter is added. Full references are given should the reader wish to obtain further information about these projections.

PREFACE TO THE THIRD EDITION

In the preparation of this edition I am once again particularly indebted to Lieutenant-Colonel Craster, who designed the Parabolic Projection and furnished me with a very complete account of it.   Mr. W. V. Lewis has also given me considerable help in checking details and in other ways.   The new diagrams have been prepared for me by Mr. E. Wrottesley.

J. A. S.

CAMBRIDGE, *March* 1933

PREFACE TO THE SECOND EDITION

IN this edition a few minor alterations have been made in the text and Appendix I has been considerably enlarged —following a suggestion by Lieutenant-Colonel J. E. E. Craster, to whom I am indebted for much help in this connection.   A short series of Trigonometrical Tables has also been added which, it is hoped, will be of use to readers.   The Tables on pages 214–222 are taken from the Four-figure Tables of Godfrey and Siddons, and are reproduced here with the permission of the Syndics of the Cambridge University Press.

J. A. S.

CAMBRIDGE, *March* 1929

PREFACE

THIS small volume is, for the most part, the fulfilment of a hobby. In developing this hobby it occurred to me that some notes on Map Projections might be of some use to students of Part I of the Geographical Tripos. But in supervising the work of such students it has been very obvious that a geographer is not necessarily a mathematician. Hence it was clear that in compiling these notes a strict limit should be placed on the knowledge of mathematics one could assume the average student to possess. It was not difficult for me to conform to this limitation. In fact, I have ventured to write these pages simply because I am not a mathematician and have every sympathy for others in a similar position.

Whilst I trust that such a confession as this will excuse the elementary treatment of the matters discussed, and also other, perhaps greater, faults, I hope, at the same time, the book may be of some value.

My original intention has been somewhat extended. The projections in common use have been described. The more difficult cases have, where possible, been approached by indirect means. Graphical constructions have also been included to help the beginner in understanding the general principles of the development of the several projections. For the same reason abundant use has been made of text figures and of worked examples.

PREFACE

The arrangement and plan of the book also call for some explanation. The division into two parts is quite arbitrary. In Part I have been included simple projections only : of the Zenithals, for example, only Polar cases and some easy Equatorial cases are considered. In Part II some of the more difficult projections are described, and also the oblique cases of some of the Zenithals. Such a separation cannot be maintained on purely logical grounds : it is solely for convenience to the beginner, who will hardly want to attempt the Oblique Gnomonic before the Polar Stereographic or the Simple Conic.

On the other hand, it may be argued that I have included in Part I several projections of no great value, and that I have described them at some length. The Orthographic is, perhaps, a case in point. Admittedly there is much to be said for this point of view. But it will be apparent that I have followed the more or less conventional way of presenting the subject. I have taken Zenithal, Conical, and Cylindrical Projections in turn, and in order to bring out the various modifications in these types I have not hesitated to give space to the less useful cases. Further, since some of the common Conventional Projections are not easily constructed, the Sinusoidal only is contained in Part I.

In Part II I have made brief reference to some uncommon projections, such as La Hire's and " La Carte Parallélogrammatique," and others. The beginner need not think it necessary to study these projections as carefully as the more usual cases. But, after all, these particular projections are types to which it seems worth while to introduce the student.

I have tried to base Part I on a step-by-step sequence.

PREFACE

To conform with this scheme, it seemed advisable to treat the Zenithals first. By doing so the student can be introduced to Perspective Projections very simply, and easy modifications lead him directly on to the nature of Equidistant and Equal-Area Projections. Further, to the beginner, the *Polar* cases of the Gnomonic, Stereographic, and Orthographic afford a very simple introduction to the application of Trigonometry.

If the reader of this book is attending a course of lectures in Cartography, he will probably obtain from them a less formal introduction to the subject. At the same time, it is hoped that the undirected student will find here material which will help him to appreciate the scope of this subject : it must be left to him to pick out those projections which are more commonly used. This he can do by reference to a good atlas and to the Table of Suitable Projections in Appendix I.

In brief, my endeavour has been to provide a working basis for the student or teacher who is not a mathematician but who wishes to understand, not only the characteristics and appearance of a graticule, but also its construction.

In conclusion, I would like to thank the many friends who have helped me. I am particularly indebted to Mr. F. Debenham, not only for writing the Introduction, but also for reading the manuscript and making many helpful and encouraging suggestions ; to Mr. P. Lake for very kindly reading and correcting parts of the typescript ; to Mr. L. A. Wickert and Instructor-Lieutenant C. R. Benstead, R.N., for checking the calculations. Most of the illustrations have been prepared by Mr. R. A. Abigail, Mr. A. H. Chapman, Mr. R. J. Lark, and Mr. J. E. Cameron ; to all I am very grateful. Finally, I would like to acknowledge the help I have received from the books noted below ; the kindness and courtesy of the publishers ; and the great help I have received from Mr. H. D. Thomas, Mr. H. Horrocks, and other friends in reading the proofs.

J. A. STEERS.

CAMBRIDGE, *May* 1926

LIST OF REFERENCES

Hinks, A. R. . Map Projections.

Garnett, W. . A Little Book on Map Projection.

Morrison, G. J. . Maps: Their Uses and Construction

Stevens, A. . . Applied Geography.

Deetz, C. H., and
   Adams, O. S. . Elements of Map Projection.

Groll, M., and
   Graf, O. . . Kartenkunde. I. Die Projektionen.

Germain . . Traité des Projections.

The Oxford Atlas (Bartholomew).

I would also acknowledge the help I have obtained from several other sources—encyclopædias, journals, etc.—too numerous to mention in detail.

Plate IX—Aitoff's Projection of the Whole Sphere—has been reproduced from the plate in Deetz and Adams's *Elements of Map Projection*, by permission of the United States Coast and Geodetic Survey.

CONTENTS

CONTENTS

CHAPTER VI

CHAPTER VII

CHAPTER VIII

CHAPTER IX

CHAPTER X

CHAPTER XI

CHAPTER XII

xvi

CONTENTS

PART II

CHAPTER I

CHAPTER II

CHAPTER III

CHAPTER IV

CHAPTER V

CHAPTER VI

CONTENTS

CHAPTER VII

CHAPTER VIII

CHAPTER IX

CHAPTER X

CHAPTER XI

CHAPTER XII

APPENDICES

ILLUSTRATIONS

PLATES

FIGURES IN THE TEXT

xix

FIGURES IN THE TEXT

FIGURES IN THE TEXT

FIGURES IN THE TEXT

FIGURES IN THE TEXT

PART I

Figures 16, 26, 32, 34, 54, 55, 61, 74, 76, 77 have been reduced in scale for convenience in printing. This should be borne in mind when reference is made to them.

CHAPTER I

INTRODUCTORY; PROPERTIES OF PROJECTIONS

A MAP projection is a means of representing the lines of latitude and longitude of the globe on a flat sheet of paper. Any such representation is a projection. The network thus formed is often called a graticule.

Our Earth, however, is a sphere : our maps are flat. As it is impossible to make a sheet of paper rest smoothly on a sphere, so it is impossible to make a correct map on a sheet of paper. It is for this reason that projections have become necessary. A casual inspection of a good atlas will show that there are several different kinds of projections. In some the lines of latitude and longitude are straight, in others curved, and yet again, the meridians may be straight and the parallels curved, and so on. By making these several selections, however, certain advantages may be obtained, so that particular countries are better represented on some one projection than on another.

Although it is impossible to make a correct map of any part of the globe, it is by no means difficult to maintain certain definite qualities in a projection. These qualities may be enumerated as follows :

Preservation of Area.
        ,,   ,, Shape (orthomorphism).
        ,,   ,, Scale.
        ,,   ,, Bearing.
Ease of Drawing.

In order that a map (after reduction is made for scale) may be equal in area with that part of the globe which it represents, shape must be neglected. A combination of true shape and correct area is impossible. But it is a comparatively simple matter to make one surface equal in area to another if it does not matter how much shape is discounted. For example, a rectangle whose sides are 1 inch and 4 inches is of the same area as a square on a base 2 inches long. Again, two parallelograms on the same base and between the same parallels are equal in area. By easy calculation a circle may be made to enclose a space equal to the surface dimensions of a sphere. Many similar examples might be given, but these are sufficient to show that the preservation of area alone is not a difficult matter.

The quality of orthomorphism is rather more difficult. If a map is correct in shape in all details, then it must be a true map. But this is impossible, and hence the term is, perhaps, rather misleading. Orthomorphism really applies only to small areas. Theoretically it applies only to points, but with this finer distinction we need not concern ourselves in this place. In order that shape may be maintained, two factors must be considered: (1) the meridians and parallels are at right angles to one another on the globe, and, in an orthomorphic projection, they must be so on the map as well; and (2) at any one point the scale is the same in all directions, but may vary from point to point.

Mr. Hinks in his *Map Projections* gives the examples of orthomorphism shown in Fig. 1.

Let A represent a strip of country along a meridian, divided into equal parts by the parallel X. This strip is rendered orthomorphically in B and C. In each case the angles are still right angles, and at any point such as X the scale along parallel and meridian has been exaggerated equally. But C is better than B, in that the meridians are straight lines, whereas they are not in B.

The question of scale is dealt with more fully in another chapter. We may here define scale as the ratio of map to ground. It is, again, an impossibility to have the scale correct in all parts of a map, but it is quite possible to make the meridians true, or the parallels true, or certain of the parallels and meridians.

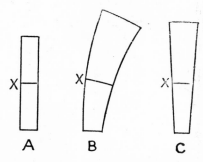

Fig. 1.—Diagrams illustrating Orthomorphism (*after Hinks*).

The preservation of correct bearings or azimuths is often an important matter, particularly in navigation. In this place it is not possible to discuss the question fully, but it may be said at once that the simplest case is the preservation of true bearings from the centre of the map. When this centre coincides with the North or South Pole, the azimuths will coincide with the meridians. The particular case of the Mercator Chart is discussed in Chapter X.

Lastly, we must consider the actual drawing of the projection. At the same time a word may be added concerning the calculations required in some graticules.

Other things being equal, it may be said at once that that projection which requires least calculation and which is most easily drawn will be chosen for a particular map rather than a more complicated case. The calculations, however, are not the concern of the draughtsman, but of the mathematician. Clearly it is easier to draw straight lines and arcs of circles than more complex curves. This consideration, while very practical, is theoretically unsound, because many of the more difficult projections to draw are not only more elegant, but at the same time better suited to the country to be mapped. Further details on this matter are given in Chapter XII.

CHAPTER II

SYSTEMS OF PROJECTIONS

THE term *projection*, in the cartographical sense, does not necessarily imply perspective or " geometrical " projection. For our purpose the word means the representation of any object on a plane. We are concerned with the various ways of delineating the parallels and meridians of the sphere on a plane.

Let us consider first a simple case. Imagine a source of light at the centre of the globe, and, further, suppose it possible for this light to throw out as shadows the meridians and parallels, as well as the forms of the continents and oceans, on to a flat sheet. For the sake of simplicity we will suppose our sheet to touch the sphere at the North Pole. We should find that the meridians were projected as straight lines and the parallels as circles. But, whereas the parallels of latitude are equidistant on the earth's surface, the distance between them would increase from the centre on our projection.

By shifting either the position of the light or the sheet of paper, we could modify our " shadow " map very considerably. We might, for example, place the light at the South Pole, and place the plane so as to bisect the sphere, e.g. in the plane of the Equator.[1] Again, the plane might be made to touch the sphere

---

[1] In this case the " shadows " must be regarded as " reflected back " on to the plane.

at some other point than the North Pole. However, as long as we project the features of the earth as shadows, we shall obtain some form of perspective or geometrical projection on the plane.

Projections made on to a plane in this way are called Zenithal or Azimuthal Projections. An azimuth is a true bearing, and bearings are all true from the centre of any zenithal projection. We have said, however, that our plane need not necessarily touch the globe at the Poles. It may touch at a point on the Equator, or at a point between the Equator and the Poles. These three cases may be termed Normal (i.e. Polar), Equatorial, and Oblique.

So far we have considered only the perspective zenithal projections. Whereas these are projections in the strict sense of the word, they are not always very satisfactory. Modifications may be made so that areas are maintained correctly, or, again, distances preserved. The nature of the modifications involved is considered elsewhere, but it may be said immediately that the modified or non-perspective forms are the more important, and, as in the case of the perspective forms, there are normal, equatorial, and oblique cases.

There are, however, other surfaces on which projections may be constructed. A sheet of paper may be rolled up to form a simple cone, which may be placed on a globe of convenient size. If the apex of the cone lies on the axis of the earth produced, the cone will rest along a line of latitude. This is the normal case. Conceivably a cone could be placed in as many positions as the plane in the zenithal projections, but the normal case is the only one that gives a useful map. As with the zenithals, we may imagine perspective and non-perspective forms, but in the case of the conical projections only the non-perspective forms are of any value.

The third system of projections may be called Cylindrical Projections. In these we may imagine a sheet of paper rolled into a tube form and placed round a globe. As in the two previous cases, we may have perspective and non-perspective forms, as well as polar, equatorial, and oblique cases. But the most useful types are the non-perspective equatorial cases.

Apart from these three generalised types, there is a large and important class that cannot be related to any of them. We may call these Conventional Projections, and include in their number some much-modified conical projections. Projections in this class vary considerably in construction and appearance, but are very widely used. This is due largely to the fact that the modifications in several cases are such as to give equal areas in a form convenient for atlas maps. Further, this class includes the projection used for the International One-in-a-Million map and also projections suitable for topographic surveys.

In conclusion, we may give in tabular form a generalised classification of projections, paying attention only to those cases which are of direct use :

1. Zenithal Projections $\begin{cases} \text{Perspective} \\ \text{Non-perspective} \end{cases} \begin{cases} \text{Normal.} \\ \text{Oblique.} \\ \text{Equatorial.} \end{cases}$

2. Conical Projections   Non-perspective. Normal.

3. Cylindrical Projections Non-perspective $\begin{cases} \text{Equatorial.} \\ \text{Transverse.} \end{cases}$

4. Conventional and Modified Conical Projections.

CHAPTER III

PART 1. AREAS

In the study of map projections we are much concerned with the question of area and how to make areas on a sheet of paper equal to areas on a globe, or a cone, or a cylinder, reduction being made for scale. Thus it is most important that the beginner should have some knowledge of this subject, and it is with this view that the following chapter is written.

Area of a Rectangle.—The simplest case is the rectangle.

Fig. 2.—Area of a Rectangle.

If we know the length of two adjacent sides, the area is found by multiplying them together. In fig. 2 the area is found by multiplying the length of AB by that of AD or BC. The square is a particular case of the rectangle.

Area of a Triangle.—The triangle is equally simple. Its area is half that of a rectangle having the same base and altitude. In fig. 3 ABC and AKVC are on the same base AC and of the same altitude DB.

It is clear that ABD = ½AKBD and DBC = ½DBVC. In other words, ABC = ½AKVC, or the base × ½ the altitude (BD), or the altitude (BD) × ½ base = ½a × b.

Area of a Polygon.—Having found the area of a tri-

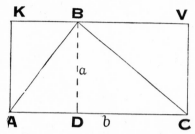

Fig. 3.—Area of a Triangle.

angle, we can at once proceed to find the area of any regular or irregular figure enclosed by straight sides. All that is necessary is to divide the figure up into a series of triangles, and the area of the whole figure is the sum of the area of the triangles. The area of the

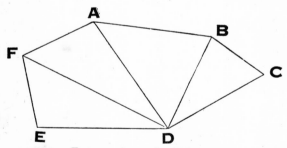

Fig. 4.—Area of a Polygon.

figure ABCDEF = total area of the triangles BCD, BDA, ADF, FDE (fig. 4).

Area of a Circle.— The area of a triangle is also the first step in finding the area of a circle. Let

ABC be a circle, with centre O. Divide the circumference into any number—*n*—of equal parts, AB being one of them. Join OA and OB. The area of the triangle OAB = AN × NO, ($\frac{1}{2}$ base × altitude).

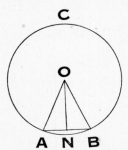

Consequently the area of the polygon thus formed $= \frac{n}{2}$ AB × ON, or *n* × AN × ON (fig. 5).

If the parts around the circumference are made infinitely small, each chord, such as AB, will finally become the same length as the arc AB—in other words, the perimeters of the polygon and of the circle have coincided—or *n* × AB = $2\pi r$.

A N B

FIG. 5.—Area of a Circle.

Also the perp. ON finally coincides with radii OA and OB.

Therefore area of circle

= area of polygon of infinitely small sides
= *n* × AB × ON/2
= $2\pi r$ × *r*/2 (because in final stage ON becomes a radius)
= πr^2.

AREA CIRCLE

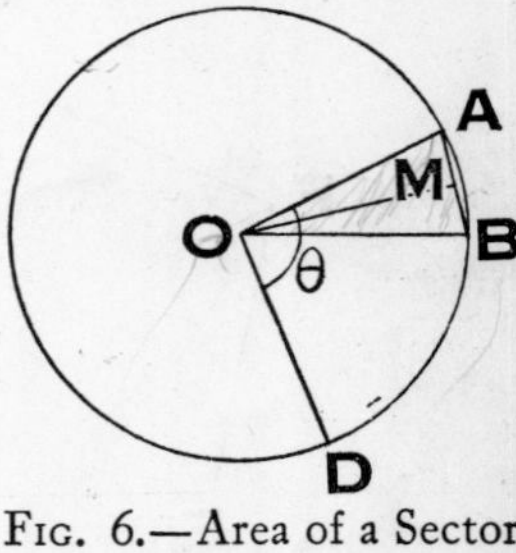

Area of a Sector.—The area of a whole circle has been shown to be πr^2. Let OAD be any sector, divided into *n* equal parts, such as OAB (fig. 6).

FIG. 6.—Area of a Sector

Now, area of the triangle OAB = AM × OM = $\frac{1}{2}$AB × OM and the area of the other triangles is the same But, as in the circle, the part AB may be made infinitely small, and then the arc AB will equal the chord AB

12

Consequently, the area of the whole sector is equal to the area of the constituent triangles:

$$\text{Area of sector} = n \times \text{AM} \times \text{OM}$$

and, as in the final stage OM becomes equal to r, the radius of the circle,

$$\text{Area} = n \times \text{AM} \times r$$
$$= r \times \tfrac{1}{2} \text{(length of arc)}.$$

Trigonometrically, if θ = circular measure of the angle AOD,

$$\text{we have arc AD} = r\theta$$
$$\text{and area of sector} = \tfrac{1}{2}r\theta \times r$$
$$= \tfrac{1}{2}r^2\theta. \text{ (See Appendix II.)}$$

SUPERFICIES OR SURFACE AREAS OF SOLID FIGURES

The Area of a Parallelopiped.—The simplest case is the parallelopiped—a figure bounded by three pairs of parallel planes. The cube is a special case.

The area of each face of a cube is found by multiplying length by breadth. The area of each face of a parallelogram is found by multiplying one side by its perpendicular distance from the opposite side. Therefore, to find the surface area of a parallelopiped, find the area of each of its faces and sum the results.

The Area of a Pyramid.—A pyramid (also a tetrahedron) is a figure all of whose faces except one meet in a point called the vertex. All the faces, except in most cases the base, of such a figure are triangles. The area can be found by finding the area of each face and adding the sums together. The area of more complex figures bounded by plane faces can be obtained similarly. Find the area of each face, either by direct methods or by dividing it up into triangles, and add together the sums thus obtained.

The Area of a Cylinder.—Let fig. 7 represent a cylinder. The area of the base is πr^2. The height of the cylinder is MN. Consider the cylinder cut along MN and unrolled. Clearly we have a rectangle whose height is MN, which is the same as that of the cylinder, and whose length is equal to the circumference of the base or of the top of the cylinder. The length of the circumference of a circle is $2\pi r$, and if the height of the cylinder be called h, the area of the curved surface of the cylinder is $2\pi rh$.

If the two ends are included, the area is $2\pi rh + 2\pi r^2$.

The Area of a Cone.—The area of a cone is, for the present purpose, very important. Let ABC (fig. 8) be a cone. V is the mid-point of the base, and AV is perpendicular to the base.

Call AB, l, and VC, r.

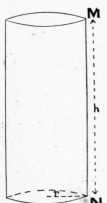

Fig. 7.—Area of a Cylinder.

The surface of the cone may be regarded as made up of an infinite number of triangles of which AXY is one. The common vertex of all such triangles is A. The altitude of all triangles is the slant height of the cone, l.

Thus the curved surface is equal to the sum of the triangles

$= \frac{1}{2}$ rectangle contained by l, and sum of the bases
$= \frac{1}{2}l \times$ circumference of the base
$= \pi rl$, where r is the radius of the base.

The area of a cone may be found by another method, a method of rather more common use in projections.

" Unwrap " or develop a cone, and a sector of a circle is formed (fig. 9).[1] If the angle θ contained by the bounding radii is known, then the area is $\frac{1}{2}l^2\theta$ (see page 13). Should it be necessary to find the area of the whole surface of the cone, add the area of the base to that of the curved surface : $\pi r l + \pi r^2$ or $\frac{1}{2}l^2\theta + \pi r^2$.

The Area of a Frustum of a Cone.—One further step is necessary before considering the area of a sphere—to find the area of the curved surface of the frustum of a cone. A frustum is defined as the volume between two parallel planes. In fig. 10 we want to find the area of the portion BCED.

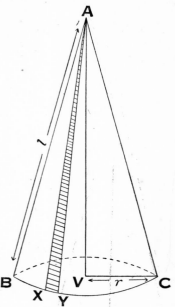

Fig. 8.—Area of a Cone.

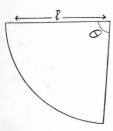

Fig. 9.—Area of a Cone.

r_1 is the radius of the end DE
r the radius of the end BC
l is the slant length of the side DB.

Let BA $= x$.

[1] A cone may be cut along a straight line joining apex to base, and then unrolled or " developed." Surfaces such as this are called " developable surfaces " (see page 64).

By similar triangles $\dfrac{x}{x+l} = \dfrac{r}{r_1}$

therefore $\qquad \dfrac{x}{l} = \dfrac{r}{r_1 - r}.$

The curved surface of the frustum BCED

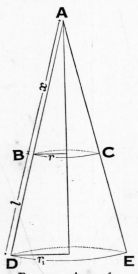

FIG. 10.—Area of a Frustum of a Cone.

= the curved surface of the cone ADE — the curved surface of the cone ABC

$= \pi r_1(x + l) - \pi r x$

$= \pi[r_1 l + x(r_1 - r)]$

$= \pi(r_1 l + rl)$

$= \pi l(r_1 + r).$

The Area of the Surface of a Sphere.—As projections have to do with the representation of the globe on flat surfaces, the method employed in finding the area of part or all of a sphere is very important.

It can be proved that the surface area of a sphere is equal to that of a circumscribed cylinder, or $= 4\pi r^2$.

In fig. 11, VO is the axis of the circumscribing cylinder. S'Y'N'W' and SYNW are corresponding belts on the cylinder and the sphere.

T is the mid-point of SW, and TK is perp. to OV. If WS be regarded as a straight line, we may look upon WSYN as a frustum of a cone, whose area is equal to $\pi l(r_1 + r)$, where $l = $ WS, $r_1 = $ WD, and $r = $ SE.

Thus area of frustum $= 2\pi \times $ TK $\times$ WS, for the curved surface of the frustum of a cone $= 2\pi \left(\dfrac{r_1 + r}{2}\right) l,$

or $2\pi l \times$ the arithmetic mean of the radii at each end of the frustum—in this case SE and WD, whose mean is TK.

LW is parallel to S'W', and SW is perp. to TO, because T is the mid-point of WS.

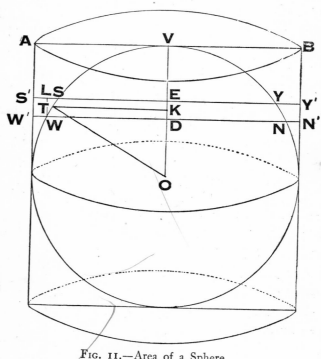

Fig. 11.—Area of a Sphere.

Also $\angle WSL = \angle STK$, since LE ‖ TK.
And $\angle STK = 90° - \angle KTO$
$= \angle TOK.$

Therefore, the triangles WLS and TOK are similar

„ $\quad TO/TK = WS/WL = WS/W'S'$

„ $\quad TK \times WS = TO \times W'S'$

Therefore, the surface generated or described by WS

$$= 2\pi \times \text{TO} \times \text{W'S'}$$
$$= 2\pi \times \text{W'D} \times \text{W'S'}$$
$$= \text{surface generated by W'S'}.$$

In the same way other belts are generated.

The conclusion is thus reached that the surface of a sphere is equal to that of a circumscribed cylinder, i.e. to $4\pi r^2$ (since $h = 2r$).

In other words, the area of a sphere is four times the area of a great circle—a circle passing entirely round the sphere and whose plane passes through the centre of the sphere.

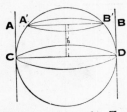

FIG. 12.—Area of a Zone of a Sphere.

The Area of a Zone.—The area of a zone or belt of a sphere is obtained in a similar manner. Let A'B'DC be any such zone. Its height is equal to the height of the corresponding zone on a cylinder (fig. 12).

Call the height of this zone h.

Now, the area of this zone

$$= \text{that of the corresponding one on the cylinder}$$
$$= \text{ABCD}$$
$$= 2\pi rh.$$

Therefore, the area of a zone $= 2\pi rh$, or the circumference of the great circle $\times$ by the height of the zone. Reference to fig. 14 shows that $h = \text{R} \sin \phi$.

∴ Area of a zone on a globe of radius $\text{R} = 2\pi \text{R} \times \text{R} \sin \phi = 2\pi \text{R}^2 \sin \phi$.

PART 2. LATITUDE AND LONGITUDE

When we think of maps and map projections, we imply a knowledge of latitude and longitude. A map cannot be drawn unless the parallels and meridians are first plotted, because all places on the Earth's surface are defined by these means.

We speak of a place in, say, lat. 50° N. What do we mean? We picture a line called 50° passing through this place and we know this line is parallel to the Equator, which is also a line of latitude numbered 0°. If we take a point on lat. 50° and another on lat. 0°, both points being on a plane through the axis of the globe,[1] and join both to the centre of the globe, we shall find that the angle made is 50°. Thus "latitude" may be defined as angular distance north or south of the Equator. A parallel of latitude is an imaginary line drawn round the Earth parallel to

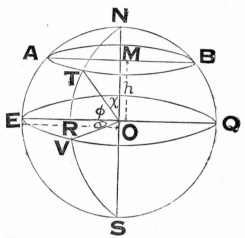

Fig. 13.—Diagram illustrating Latitude and Longitude.

the Equator and at a constant angular distance from it. Only one line of latitude—the Equator—is a great circle; all others are small circles. "Longitude" is measurement in an easterly and westerly direction. A meridian of longitude is a line passing entirely round the sphere, and through the Poles. All meridians are great circles.

Parallels and meridians intersect at right angles on the globe.

[1] In other words, the points are on the same meridian of longitude.

In fig. 13 EVQ is the Equator.

EO, the radius of the sphere, = R.

ATB is a line of latitude whose angular distance from the Equator is the angle TOV = ϕ.

The angle TON is called the polar distance or the co-latitude of T = χ = (90° − ϕ) or (90° − lat.).

SANQ and SVTN are meridians of longitude whose distance apart is the angle EOV = θ.

AM is the radius of the parallel ATB.

ABQE is a zone whose altitude is MO = h.

If we know the value of R, the radius of the globe, and the latitude of any parallel, it is a very easy matter

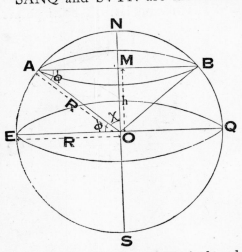

FIG. 14.—Diagram illustrating Latitude and Longitude.

to find the length of that parallel.

In fig. 14 we have the same lettering as in the previous figure, but the latter is rather more simplified.

The latitude of the parallel AB is the angle AOE = ϕ.

$$EO = AO = R.$$

Because AM is parallel to EO,

$$\text{angle MAO} = \text{angle AOE} = \phi.$$

Therefore AM = R cos ϕ.

20

But AM = radius of the parallel AB.

Therefore length of parallel AB = 2π R cos ϕ.

If the radius and length of the parallel are needed in terms of the angle AOM (the co-latitude), then AM = R sin χ, and AB = 2π R sin χ.

CHAPTER IV

SCALE

ANY atlas map, with the exception of World maps,[1] has attached to it a scale line, or a statement of the scale to be used on the map. The scale may be shown as a line divided up into units representing miles, hundreds of miles, and so on ; or it may be in the form of a fraction called the " representative fraction." In whatever way it is shown, we know that to read the map correctly we must make use of the scale intelligently.

We may define scale as the relation between a given distance on the ground and the corresponding distance on the map. Thus, if we say that a map is on a scale of 1 inch to 1 mile, we mean that an inch on the map represents a mile on the ground. Writing this as a (representative) fraction, we have 1/63,360, the denominator being the number of inches in a mile. It is worthy of notice, however, that 1/63,360 or any other fraction means that one unit (numerator) on the map represents so many—63,360 in this case—units (denominator) on the ground. Directly we use a fraction instead of a statement, such as 1 inch to 1 mile, we free ourselves from any one particular unit of measurement, and in return have a ratio expressing the relation between map and ground in any unit of measurement. Thus 1/100,000

[1] Mercator's Chart is sometimes accompanied by a scale which is adjusted to each line of latitude.

means that 1 unit, be it inch, centimetre, or any other unit, represents 100,000 inches, centimetres, etc., on the ground.

In one sense, therefore, we may define a map as a reduced representation of a part or all of the globe. But the globe is a sphere and a map is made on a flat sheet of paper. This contrast leads us to one rather puzzling feature in the question of scale. If we were to make a small map of East Anglia, we need hardly take into consideration the curvature of the earth. The area of the district is so small and the globe is so large, that, to all intents and purposes, East Anglia may be regarded as flat. But if we were to map the district on a very large scale we should begin to notice discrepancies creeping in, because on this scale we have room to make allowance for the curvature of the Earth.

We can approach the problem from another point of view. If we have a globe we can stick a small piece of paper to it in such a way that it does not crease to any noticeable extent. This implies that the area on which the paper rests could be, on the scale of that globe, represented nearly correctly on a flat surface of the size of the paper. Now imagine a very much larger globe. The area over which the paper rested in the first instance has now expanded in a certain proportion, and thus in order to cover it we must expand the sheet of paper in corresponding proportion. But if we were to experiment on this second globe with the larger piece of paper, we should find that the paper would not lie as " flat " as in the first case. The little crumples, which were then so small as to be practically unnoticeable, are now greatly magnified, their size having increased in the same proportion as the paper, and they are now of such magnitude as to be conspicuous.

Thus it is that any map of a small area and on a scale likely to occur in an ordinary atlas is virtually correct. On the other hand, if, instead of increasing our globe, we increase the paper alone, we shall find that we cannot cover a large area without very considerable folding. If we try to stick a piece of paper over Asia on any globe, we shall find that we cannot do so without greatly distorting the paper.

So far we have considered scale only with reference to the curvature of the globe. One other point must not be omitted. A map, after all, is, by the nature of things, only a picture of the ground. We can reduce objects to scale, but we cannot do this *ad infinitum*. The average draughtsman cannot do more than produce lines as fine as 1/100th of an inch. Now, if we are working on a scale of 1 inch to 1 mile, we have 1 inch representing 5,280 feet, or 1/100th of an inch representing 52·8 feet. Now, 1/63,360 is a large scale, and is never reached in ordinary atlas maps. But even with so large a scale we are unable to reduce all objects correctly. For example, most main roads are about 40 or 50 feet wide : if we were to draw them correct to scale on a 1-inch map, they would appear as lines 1/100th of an inch thick. But because of their great importance this is inconvenient—and, therefore, they are much exaggerated on a map.

On an atlas map only the very big and important features can be shown, but even then we are faced with the same difficulty. Rivers afford a good example : the Amazon is one of the main physical features of South America. An ordinary scale for South America on an atlas is 1/17,000,000.[1] On this scale a mile is represented by a line 0·00373 inches long. In its upper and middle courses the Amazon is often more than a mile wide, but no cartographer would try to show it as a sinuous line 3/1,000ths of an inch thick.

Therefore, we are forced to the conclusion that the question of scale is of the utmost importance. We may reduce the scale, but we cannot increase the fineness of our draughtsmanship. For small maps we must allow more to be shown conventionally than for large-scale maps.

So much for the general problem. Let us now turn to the application of it in the construction of map projections.

The position of any place on the globe is determined by its latitude and longitude. If, then, we can draw in the parallels and the meridians in the way we require them, on a sheet of paper, the country can be sketched in afterwards. In approaching the problems of scale and projection it will be well to concentrate wholly on the parallels and the meridians, and not to worry about the outlines of lands and seas.

Eratosthenes gave us our first good measurement of the radius and of the circumference of the globe, but even now we really do not know the exact form. However, that matters little here, because the more exacting refinements of Geodesy cannot be shown on an ordinary map. For our purposes we shall assume the earth is a ball whose mean radius is 3,960 miles or 250,905,600 inches.[2] For practical purposes we shall call this

[1] The scale used in Bartholomew's *Oxford Atlas*.
[2] Chauvenet and Loomis give 20,889,000 feet as the radius of the earth.

250,000,000 inches—the odd thousands making no appreciable difference for ordinary scales.

Imagine a globe having a radius of 250,000,000 inches. If we wish to make a globe 1/250,000,000th the size of the Earth, we must divide the radius of the Earth by 250,000,000—in which case we have 1 inch. In other words, a small globe of 1 inch radius is 1/250,000,000th of the size of the Earth itself, i.e. taking the radius as the unit of measurement. [The area of the sphere is $4\pi R^2$, the volume $\frac{4}{3}\pi R^3$.]

On the Equator of the Earth a degree of longitude is 1/360th of the whole circumference—or nearly 70 miles. On a globe on a scale of 1/250,000,000 a degree of longitude will be 250,000,000 times smaller, and we must express the amount in some small unit such as a fraction of an inch or of a millimetre. As we are assuming that the Earth is a true sphere, it follows that degrees of latitude measured along the meridians are of the same length as degrees of longitude measured along the Equator.

Again, if we require a map on a scale of 1/1,000,000 we see at once that the radius of a globe on this scale is 250 inches. The length of the Equator on such a globe is $2\pi R$, or $2 \times 3\cdot1416 \times 250$ inches, and 1 degree of longitude on this globe (measured along the Equator) is $2\pi R/360$ or $2 \times 3\cdot1416 \times 250/360$ inches; similarly for the length of a degree of latitude measured along the meridians. If we want to find the length of any other line of latitude we make use of the formula given on page 21 :

Length of a line of latitude = $2\pi R$ cos lat.

The length of the 50th parallel on a scale of 1/1,000,000

$= 2\pi R \cos 50°$, where $R = 250$ inches

$= 2 \times 3·1416 \times 250 \times 0·6428$ inches.

And 1 degree of longitude along this line

$= 2 \times 3·1416 \times 250 \times 0·6428/360$ inches.

Having found the lengths of any lines or parts of lines that we need, we plot them on paper and in this way build up a network. Of course, not all lines thus plotted will be true to scale ; if they were, we should have a correct map, which is, *ipso facto*, impossible. However, the following pages will make this point clearer, but in the actual question of scale nothing more is involved than given here.

CHAPTER V

PART 1. ZENITHAL OR AZIMUTHAL PROJECTIONS

THESE projections are made upon a plane tangent to the globe at any point. Usually the point is taken at one of the Poles or at some place on the Equator; it can, however, be taken at any other point, but, if it is, the projection is more difficult to make.

A sub-division may be made into perspective and non-perspective zenithals. In the former the constructions are most easily visualised if one imagines a transparent globe, with the surface features painted on it, placed in various positions relative to a point of light. If the light be inside the Earth—at the centre—we have the Gnomonic; if at one end of a diameter, the Stereographic; if at an infinite distance away, the Orthographic. In this last case all the rays are supposed to be parallel. These relationships are easily seen by means of three diagrams (fig. 15, A, B, C). (In each case XY is the plane of projection and O the source of light.)

It can be seen at once that these are merely special cases: the source of light can be moved to any other position, as in the cases of La Hire, Sir H. James, Clarke and others. La Hire takes the source of light at 1·71 times the radius of the Earth, Sir H. James at 1·36 times the radius, and the several points that Clarke took varied between 1·65 and 1·35 times the radius. By so

28

altering the position of the light certain advantages are obtained—but their study involves a knowledge of higher mathematics and cannot be considered here. In

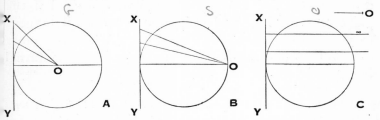

FIG. 15.—Simple Perspective Zenithal Projections.

any case these particular projections are very seldom used (fig. 16).

The non-geometrical zenithals include the zenithal equidistant and the zenithal equal-area. In the polar case of the former, the distances along the meridians are

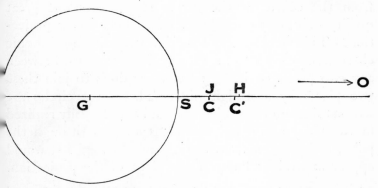

FIG. 16.—Points of Projection of certain Zenithals.

the same as on the globe, reduction being made for scale; and on the latter, the area between any two parallels is made the same as on the globe. All zenithals possess the property of maintaining azimuths, or true bearings from the centre of the map, correct. This is most easily visualised in the polar cases, because the meridians all radiate out from the Pole at their correct angular distance apart. The same property holds good if the plane on which the projection is constructed is tangent to the globe at any other point, but only in the polar case will the meridians correspond with the azimuthal lines.[1]

PART 2. THE GNOMONIC OR CENTRAL PROJECTION

This is a zenithal projection of the perspective type. The source of light is at the centre of the globe, and the plane on which the projection is made is tangent to the globe at some point—usually at one of the Poles or on the Equator, though it can be anywhere else.

The projection is unsuited for large areas, because the exaggeration of the scale increases very rapidly away from the centre of the map. It possesses one great quality—all great circles are straight lines on the projection. This means to say that if we are using a gnomonic chart and we wish to find the shortest distance between any two places on it, all we have to do is to join these two places by a straight line. That great circles are straight lines on the projection can be most easily realized in the polar case : the meridians all pass through the poles, and, as seen from the centre of the globe, would appear as straight lines on the plane of the projection.

[1] It is important to realise at the outset that a zenithal projection of any sort can be used for a country just as well as for a hemisphere. The beginner may be misled by the fact that, e.g. the zenithal equal-area projection, which so often figures in atlases for the " World in Hemispheres," is not commonly used for any other map. Africa—and other areas—can be mapped on any of the zenithals, though, necessarily, certain countries are better suited to them than others.

THE GNOMONIC PROJECTION

he student should try to visualise this and the other
vo cases: (1) when the plane of the projection is
ngent to the Earth at some point on the Equator,
id (2) when it is tangent at a point between the Poles
id the Equator.[1]

The projection is seldom used in atlases, on account
f the great exaggeration. It is sometimes used for
arts of small areas, and the recent advances in air
avigation have tended to popularise it to some extent,
though Mercator's Projection is used officially for air
aps.

POLAR CASE

Graphical Construction

In fig. 17 the method is illustrated. Draw a circle
) scale to represent the Earth and from its centre draw
dii at the required angles, such as OB, OA, OD, and
ontinue these lines to the plane D'D', which is tangent
) the Earth at the North Pole. The radii for drawing
ie concentric circles representing the parallels can be
ken off directly with a pair of compasses: NB' is the
dius for 70°, because the angle NOB is 20°, or the
omplement of 70°. The meridians are constructed
ith the help of a protractor, by laying off angles equal
) the required interval of longitude from N as centre.

Trigonometrical Construction

The polar case is very easy. A plane is supposed to

[1] That ALL great circles project into straight lines follows from the
ct that any great circle lies in a plane through the centre of the globe,
iich is the centre of projection. The great circle must therefore project
to the line of intersection of its plane with the plane of the projection,
▸ matter where the plane of projection may be.

touch the globe at one of the Poles, and points on th
surface of the Earth are projected geometrically on t
this plane from the centre of the globe.

It is clear from fig. 17 that places situated far from
the Pole are much distorted on the projection. D **i**

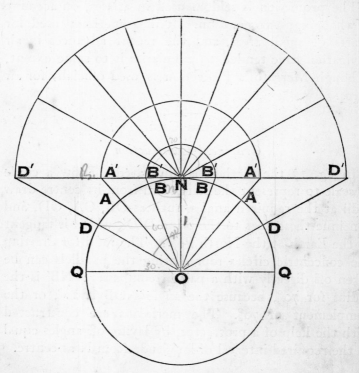

FIG. 17.—Graphical Construction of Polar Gnomonic.

30° from the Equator or 60° from the Pole. In th
figure the radius of the Globe is 1 inch; the distanc
ND along the Earth is then $2\pi R/6$ or $1·0472$ inches
But D is projected on the plane as D'. Now, ND
is equal to NO tan (angle NOD'), or R tan 60°, o

1·7321 inches—an exaggeration of 0·6849 inches. Further, the Equator cannot be represented on the projection, because, as seen in the diagram, QQ is parallel to D'D', and therefore the projection of Q cannot reach the plane.

To make the polar map, all that is necessary is to

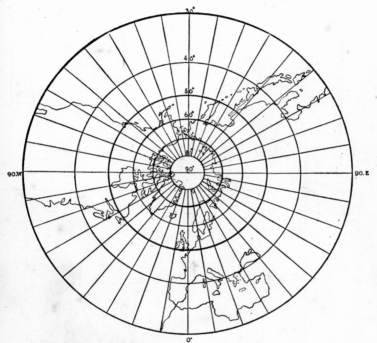

FIG. 18.—Gnomonic Map of North Polar Areas.

make a table of the tangents of the angles NOB, NOA, etc. (i.e. the tangents of the co-latitudes or the co-tangents of the latitudes), for as many degrees as required and multiply these by the radius of the Earth, reduction being made for scale. These are marked off along a line which is taken as a meridian, and concentric circles are drawn through each separate point. The meridians are spaced off with a protractor (fig. 18).

EQUATORIAL CASE
Graphical Construction

The graphical construction of the equatorial gnomonic

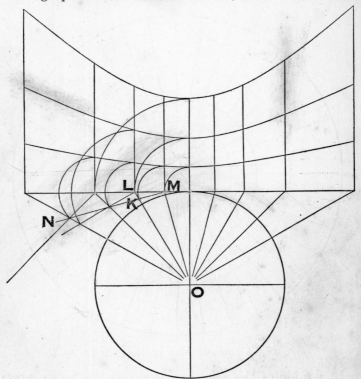

FIG. 19.—Graphical Construction of Equatorial Gnomonic.

is rather more complicated than that of the polar case. A circle is drawn to scale to represent the Earth. Degrees from the centre of the circle are then laid off with a protractor as before. The divisions along the Equator and

THE GNOMONIC PROJECTION

along the central meridian are obtained as for the parallels in the polar case. To find the spaces on any other meridian (fig. 19), draw a line such as MN at right angles to OM at the point M. The divisions MK, etc., will then give the required points along that particular meridian. By doing the same for every other meridian, a complete graticule can be constructed.

Trigonometrical Construction

The same general principles hold good as in the polar case. If a plane is made to touch the sphere on the Equator, it is easy to see that along the Equator the meridians will be spaced just as were the parallels in the polar map —i.e. at distances from the central meridian varying as the tangents

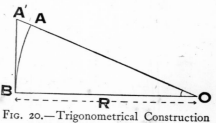

FIG. 20.—Trigonometrical Construction of Equatorial Gnomonic.

of the angles of longitude. Similarly, the distances of the parallels of latitude along the central meridian from the Equator must vary as the tangents of the angles of latitude.

The main difficulty, however, is to draw in the other parallels, which are not great circles and, therefore, not straight lines on the projection ; they are, in fact, curves convex to the Equator. In fig. 20 the projection of A is A' ; that is to say, A' is the point on the projection representing the position of the meridian of longitude A on the globe. In the polar projection it will have been noticed that all the meridians are straight lines. But all meridians are great circles, and it has already been pointed out that the planes of all great circles pass

35

through the centre of the Earth. Thus all meridians on the gnomonic projection, no matter where the plane touches the Earth, are straight lines. In fig. 21 $OA' = R \sec \theta$, i.e. the line joining the centre of the Earth O to A' is longer than the radius OB by the

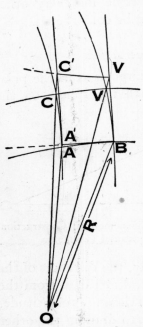

amount AA'. But on the globe a parallel of latitude always maintains a constant angular distance from the Equator. Therefore, in order to find the position of C' on the plane of projection (fig. 21) we must multiply the distance OA' by the tangent of angle C'OA', that is, the latitude of C. But OA' = OB sec A'OB = R sec (long.) ∴ C'A' = R sec (long.) tan (lat.)

In fact, we arrive at the conclusion that the position of the intersection of any meridian and parallel, apart from any point on the Equator or on the central meridian, is given by the formula R sec θ tan ϕ, where θ is the

FIG. 21.—Trigonometrical Construction of Equatorial Gnomonic.

difference in longitude between the central meridian and the meridian in question, and ϕ the difference between the Equator and the parallel in question. This is shown in fig. 21.

The matter may be put in another way. ABC (fig. 22) is the plane of the projection. DE is the meridian of longitude θ, measured from the central meridian, EA. DE projects into BC.

36

THE GNOMONIC PROJECTION

The Equator projects into AB.

GF is a parallel of latitude ϕ.

Then F (lat. ϕ, long. θ) projects into C, on BC, and BC = OB tan BOC = OB tan ϕ.

But OB = OA sec AOB = R sec θ.

$\therefore$ BC = R tan ϕ sec θ.

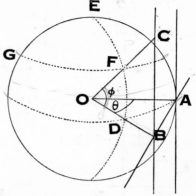

FIG. 22.—Trigonometrical Construction of Equatorial Gnomonic.

The conclusion is reached that the point in lat. ϕ, long. θ, projects into the point C on the straight line BC, corresponding to the meridian (long. θ). AB corresponds to the Equator, and AD to the central meridian, and BC = R sec θ tan ϕ (fig. 23).

In the equatorial gnomonic the parallels will be curves drawn through fixed points which represent the intersections of the meridians and the parallels.

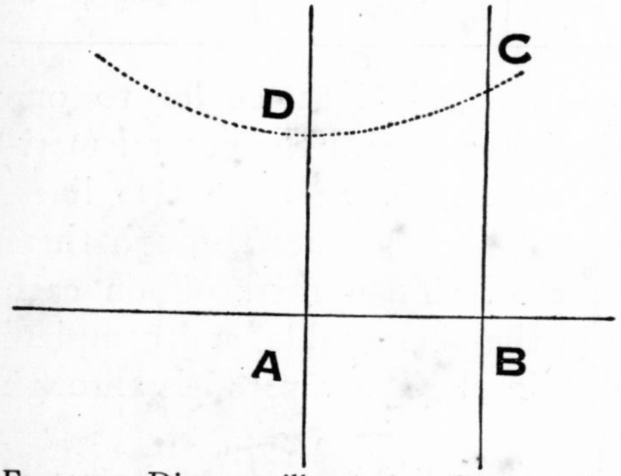

Computation of an Example.—A map of Africa is to be made on the gnomonic projection: scale 1/250,000,000.

FIG. 23.—Diagram illustrating Construction of Parallels on Equatorial Gnomonic.

Meridians and parallels at 10° intervals. The central meridian is 15° E. longitude.

The meridians to be shown are: west longitude, 25°, 15°, 5°; east longitude, 5°, 15°, 25°, 35°, 45°, 55°. The parallels, both north and south, are: 0°, 10°, 20°, 30°, 40°.

The divisions along the central meridian and the Equator will be

$$R \tan 10° = 0.1763 \text{ inches.}$$
$$R \tan 20° = 0.3640 \quad ,,$$
$$R \tan 30° = 0.5774 \quad ,,$$
$$R \tan 40° = 0.8391 \quad ,,$$

The divisions along the other meridians for spacing the parallels will be:

5° E. and 25° E.	5° W. and 35° E.	15° W. and 45° E.	25° W. and 55° E.
$R \sec 10° \tan 10°$ = 0.1790	$R \sec 20° \tan 10°$ = 0.1876	$R \sec 30° \tan 10°$ = 0.2036	$R \sec 40° \tan 10°$ = 0.2301
$R \sec 10° \tan 20°$ = 0.3696	$R \sec 20° \tan 20°$ = 0.3874	$R \sec 30° \tan 20°$ = 0.4204	$R \sec 40° \tan 20°$ = 0.4751
$R \sec 10° \tan 30°$ = 0.5863	$R \sec 20° \tan 30°$ = 0.6144	$R \sec 30° \tan 30°$ =0.6667	$R \sec 40° \tan 30°$ = 0.7537
$R \sec 10° \tan 40°$ = 0.8519	$R \sec 20° \tan 40°$ = 0.8930	$R \sec 30° \tan 40°$ = 0.9690	$R \sec 40° \tan 40°$ = 1.0954

To Plot.—Draw two lines at right angles to one another to represent the Equator and the central meridian. Then mark off tangents along these two lines, and draw the meridians as straight lines through these divisions along the Equator. Then mark off on each meridian the distances in the above table, and complete the graticule by drawing in the other parallels through corresponding points.

(It is well to remember that divisions east and west of the central meridian and north and south of the Equator are similar.)

Finally, the outline of the map is drawn in.

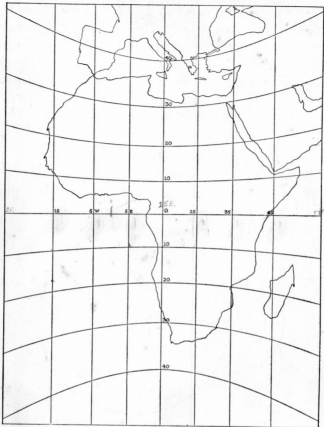

Fig. 24.—Africa on a Gnomonic Projection.
[1/125,000,000.]

PART 3. THE STEREOGRAPHIC PROJECTION

This is another of the perspective zenithal projections. The parallels and the meridians are projected from a point at one end of a diameter on to a plane tangent at the other.   In itself the projection is not of very much use, but it is most useful in certain transformation processes, which are described later.

39

STUDY OF MAP PROJECTIONS

It can be used for maps of the World in hemispheres and also for separate continents and countries. However, its property of <u>orthomorphism</u> and the ease of its construction can hardly be said to be sufficiently favourable advantages to make it a common projection in atlases.

As in the case of the gnomonic, it can be constructed on a plane which may be tangent to the globe at any point.

POLAR CASE AND EQUATORIAL CASE
Graphical Construction of the Stereographic

This projection is constructed very simply by purely

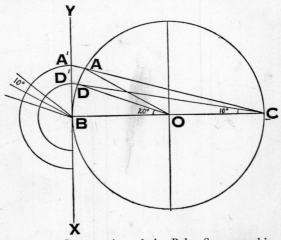

FIG. 25.—Construction of the Polar Stereographic.
(B represents the North Pole.)

graphical means. In fig. 25 the radii to draw the parallels may be found by measurement from B along XY. Thus BD′ is the radius required to draw the parallel of latitude D. By setting off from O the required angles and marking the point where these angles cut the bounding meridian, and then from C drawing lines such as

40

CDD', the required radii are found. The meridians are constructed as in the gnomonic polar case.

In the case of the equatorial stereographic the divisions between the parallels on the central meridian and between the meridians on the Equator are similar. In each case they are found just as in the polar map. All other parallels and meridians are arcs of circles and are constructed as on page 43.

THE POLAR CASE

Trigonometrical Construction

Let XY be the plane touching the globe at B, which is the North Pole (fig. 25). A is any point on the meridian BAC whose co-latitude or angular distance from the Pole is the angle AOB or χ.

By simple geometry the angle AOB = 2 × angle ACB.

BO = R, the radius of the Earth.

Then A'B = 2R tan angle ACB or 2R tan $\frac{1}{2}\chi$.

Similarly any other point such as D' can be found.

To construct the projection, describe circles with radii BD', BA', etc., and space the meridians by means of a protractor (fig. 26).

The distance between the parallels evidently increases somewhat rapidly away from the centre of the map. The Equator will obviously be at a distance from the Pole of 2R tan 45°, which is twice the radius of the globe.

THE EQUATORIAL CASE

Trigonometrical Construction

Suppose a map be made in which the point where the Greenwich meridian cuts the Equator be taken as centre. For the same reason as in the polar map, the distances apart of the meridians along the Equator and of the parallels along the central meridian will vary as the tangents of half the angles of longitude or latitude, as the case may be.

To construct the projection, draw two axes at right

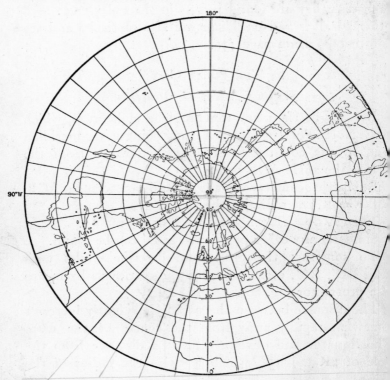

Fig. 26.—Stereographic Map of the Northern Hemisphere.
[*c.* 1/260,000,000.]

angles to one another to represent the Equator and the central meridian. Mark off along each the points where they will be cut by the meridians and parallels respectively. Having found the position of the Pole,

42

describe a circle. This will be the bounding meridian of the map, which will show a complete hemisphere. Then place a protractor at the centre of the map and mark off the required angles, and note where these cut the bounding meridian. Then, to draw the other parallels, all that is necessary is to pass a circle through the two points on the bounding meridian and the corresponding point on the central meridian. Similarly,

the meridians are constructed by passing circles through the Poles and the corresponding points on the Equator. This may be done geometrically by bisecting the chords[1] of any latitude and finding the centre of the circle in the ordinary way. This method requires careful drawing.

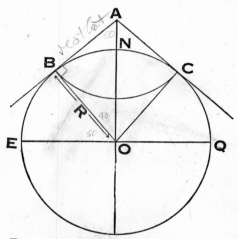

Fig. 27—Construction of Parallels on the Equatorial Stereographic.

However, to find the centres of these circles by graphical means only is an awkward process, and they are easily found trigonometrically.[2]

[1] The chords referred to are those formed by joining the two points on the bounding meridian to the corresponding point on the central meridian.
[2] The graphical construction mentioned on page 41 is the same as described in the above paragraphs, except that the position of the Poles, and therefore the insertion of the bounding meridian, is found by drawing instead of trigonometrically. The other parallels and meridians are put in in exactly the same way.

In fig. 27, B is in 50° N. lat., and on the projection 50° N. is represented by the arc BC with centre at A. But BA = R cot 50°, and AO = R cosec 50°. That is to say, the required radius is R times the cotangent of the latitude, and the distance of the centre of the arc from O, the centre of the map, is R times the cosecant of the latitude.

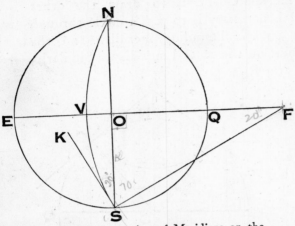

FIG. 28.—Construction of Meridians on the Equatorial Stereographic.

In fig. 28 let V be supposed to be 20° W. long. The centre of the circle required to draw the arc NVS is F. Let KS be tangent to the meridian NVS at S, then the angle KSO is equal to the angle VSO (= 20°), angles being represented correctly. FS is the required radius, and in terms of the radius of the Earth and the longitude it is R times cosecant of the angle OFS, and OFS and KSO are equal angles. The distance from the centre, O, is OF, which is R times the cotangent of the angle OFS, or, in other words, R cot longitude.[1]

[1] In figs. 27 and 28 the plane of projection is taken as the meridional plane through the centre, and at right angles to a line joining the centre of the globe to the source of light. This plane is parallel to the tangent plane indicated in fig. 25. The bounding meridian of the map is, therefore, constructed with radius R tan 45°, and not 2R tan 45°. This is merely a point of mathematical detail and does not affect the study and use of the projection, or even its construction.

THE ORTHOGRAPHIC PROJECTION

PART 4. THE ORTHOGRAPHIC PROJECTION

This is the case in which the light, or the point of projection, is at infinity. The rays of light are thus parallel. It is of little use from the geographer's point of view, but is of interest to the <u>astronomer</u>, because orthographic " maps " of the Moon and other heavenly bodies are " seen " every time he looks at such bodies.

POLAR CASE
Graphical Construction

The polar graticule is easy to make. In fig. 29 let ENQS be a circle representing the globe to scale. EQ is the Equator, N the North Pole. E′NQ′ is a plane tangent at the North Pole. A, B, C are points on the surface of the

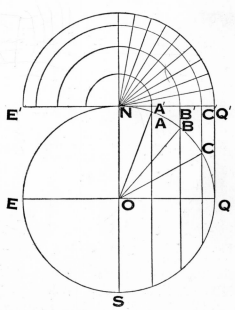

FIG. 29.—Graphical Means of Constructing the Polar Orthographic.

Earth at 20°, 40°, and 60° respectively from N. From A, B, C, etc., draw lines parallel to NS and produce them until they meet the plane in A′, B′, C′, etc. These points are then the projections of A, B, C, etc.

With centre N draw circles with radii NA′, NB′, NC′, etc., to represent the parallels of latitude, and with a

45

protractor space out the meridians. The projection is then completed.

Trigonometrical Construction

In fig. 30 E'Q' is again the plane tangent at N. ON, OB, OC are radii. B' and C' are the projections of B and C. The problem is to find the radii to draw the parallels.

Draw BX and CY parallel to OQ. Then BX = BO

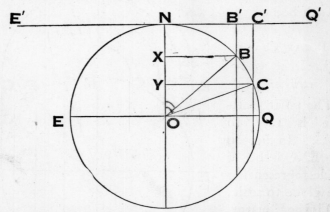

Fɪɢ. 30.—Trigonometrical Means of Constructing the Polar Orthographic.

sin angle BOX; and CY = CO sin angle COY. But XB = NB', and YC = NC'.

Thus the radii required to draw the parallels are the sines of the co-latitudes (i.e. the angle between the pole and the parallel in question). Or—in terms of the latitude—the radii are the cosines of the latitude, because the angle XBO = the angle BOQ, and the angle YCO = the angle COQ, and so on. The meridians are constructed as in the graphical method.

All, then, that is required to make an orthographic Polar projection is a table of sines or cosines.

THE ORTHOGRAPHIC PROJECTION

As an example we will compute the figures for a map of the Polar Regions on a scale of 1/50,000,000.

Clearly R, the radius of the globe on this scale, is 5 inches. Thus the radii are :

For 90° = 5 sin 0° or 5 cos 90° = 0·0000
  ,,   80° = 5 ,, 10° or 5 ,, 80° = 0·8680
  ,,   70° = 5 ,, 20° or 5 ,, 70° = 1·7100
  ,,   60° = 5 ,, 30° or 5 ,, 60° = 2·5000
  ,,   50° = 5 ,, 40° or 5 ,, 50° = 3·2140

and so on.

THE EQUATORIAL CASE
Graphical Construction

The equatorial map is not quite so easy to make graphically. The difficulty lies in obtaining the meridian curves. The spaces between the parallels on the central meridian and between the meridians on the equator are the same. This can be shown as in fig. 31.

Suppose we consider a section through the centre of the Earth and the point of contact with the plane.

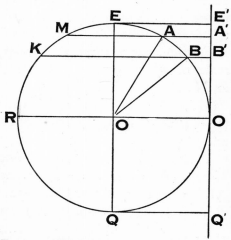

Fig. 31.—The Spacing of the Parallels and Meridians on the Equatorial Orthographic.

This plane may be taken in turn to be the equatorial plane and the plane of the central meridian.

47

In the first case the Equator projects into E′Q′ and A′B′ represents one of the divisions of the Equator by the meridians. In the second case E′Q′ represents the central meridian and A′B′ one of the divisions of the central meridian by the parallels of latitude.

But the other lines of latitude are shorter than the Equator, and, therefore, the meridian spacing is smaller. If reference is made to fig. 31, it will be seen that the length of a line of latitude, A, on the map is MA ; similarly KB is the length of parallel B. By careful drawing these lines may be measured with fair accuracy, and thus the proportion that they bear to the Equator can be found. Now, the divisions along the Equator are known, and having obtained the length of any other parallel, and knowing the divisions (also found by measurement) of any part of the Equator, we can find the corresponding divisions on any other parallel.

Consider an example : A map is to be made on a scale of 1/125,000,000, every 15th degree of latitude and of longitude to be shown.

Make a circle to scale to represent the Earth (R = 2 inches). By similarity of divisions on the Equator and on the central meridian, the spaces OA and OA′, AB and A′B′, and so on, are equal (fig. 32). Now, OE = OE′ = 2 inches. By measurement AL = 1·94 and OA′ = 0·52 inches. Thus the corresponding division (AA″) on AL is found from the ratio $\dfrac{AA''}{OA'} = \dfrac{AL}{OE'}$, whence $AA'' = \dfrac{OA' . AL}{OE'} = 0·$ inches, a figure which is sufficiently accurate for the present purpose. In the same way any other point may be found. Finally, the meridians are drawn in as curves passing through corresponding points on each parallel.

They are, in fact, ellipses. (It is a point worth memoris-ing that the parallel of 60° N. or S. is just half as long as the Equator, and consequently divisions on it are half the length of those on the Equator.)

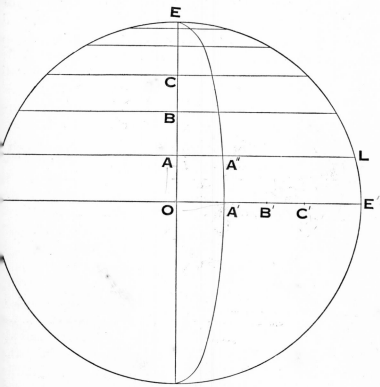

FIG. 32.—Meridians on the Equatorial Orthographic.
[*c.* 1/130,000,000.]

Trigonometrical Construction

The trigonometrical construction of the equatorial orthographic projection is also rather more difficult than the polar case. Reference to fig. 31 will show that the intervals between parallels and the Equator on the central meridian, and between meridians and the central meridian on the Equator respectively vary as the sines of the angles of latitude and longitude. Thus lat. 30° is distant from the Equator R sin 30°, measured along the central meridian, and similarly long. 30° E. or W. is R sin 30° distant from the central meridian measured along the Equator. The parallels are drawn as straight lines. The meridians are curves and are more difficult to obtain. In terms of the radius (R) the lengths of the parallels are 2R cos 10°, 20° . . . 90° where 10°, etc., is the interval of latitude. Division along the parallel are found as follows. Take as an example 40° N. Its length is 2R cos 40° = 3·0640 inches, and half its length is 1·5320 inches. With this radius multiply the sine of the angles of longitude :

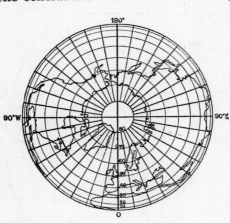

FIG. 33.—Orthographic Map of the Northern Hemisphere.
[1/250,000,000.]

Long. 20° E = 1·5320 sin 20° = 0·5240 ; long. 50° E = 1·5320 sin 50°, and so on. Divisions along any other parallel are found in the same manner (fig. 32).

Instead of this method, ellipses may be drawn through the Poles and the points marked on the Equator, because the meridians are ellipses.

PART 5. THE RELATIONS BETWEEN THE GNOMONIC, STEREOGRAPHIC, AND ORTHOGRAPHIC PROJECTIONS

In fig. 35 let O be the centre of the Earth and N the North Pole. P is any point on the surface of the

FIG. 34.—Orthographic Map of the Indian Ocean.
[*c.* 1/130,000,000.]

Earth (in this case let it be 40° from the Pole). P¹, P², P³ are its corresponding places on the plane of projection, XY, P¹ being the gnomonic, P² the stereographic, and ³ the orthographic.

The true distance of P from N is the arc PN.

In the above figure $R = 2''$,[1] and so arc $PN = R \times 40°$ (in radians) $= 1·3962''$. [Or as $40° = \frac{1}{9}$ of circumference, arc $PN = \dfrac{2\pi R}{9}$.]

On the gnomonic projection $P^1N = R \tan 40° = 1''·6782$.

On the stereographic projection $P^2N = 2R \tan 20° = 1''·4560$.

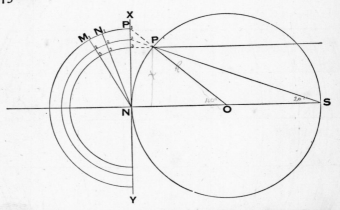

Fig. 35.—The Relations between the Polar Cases of the Gnomonic Stereographic, and Orthographic Projections.

On the orthographic projection $P^3N = R \sin 40° = 1''·2856$.

Thus it is easy to find the error per cent. for each particular projection. In the gnomonic it is found thus : Find the difference between the true distance of P from N on the globe and the distance between them on the projection ; i.e. $1''·6782 - 1''·3962 = 0''·2820$

Then the error per cent. is $\dfrac{0''·282 \times 100}{1''·3962} = 20·2\%$.

[1] In fig. 35 the scale is reduced by one-half.

THE CONSTANT OF THE CONE

t the centre of the globe and its rays shining as radii,
ve should require a very long cylinder to " catch " the
ays, and even then the poles would be left out. This
an be seen to be the case by reference to fig. 40, where
'B'C'D' are the shadows or projections of ABCD as
een from O. N and S can never be projected on the
ylinder, because the rays ON and OS are parallel to its
urface. On the other hand, EQ—the Equator—will be
f the same length, and therefore scale, on the projection
s on the globe. This will be the
nly line correct to scale. Such a
rojection as this would be a natural
" shadow " map of the earth on a
ylinder, but it would be of little
ise. However, instead of project-
ng quite so simply, it is easy to
nodify the methods and thus pro-
luce useful cylindrical maps.

Similarly a cone placed over the
lobe can be unwrapped[1] ; we
hall then have a sector of a circle.

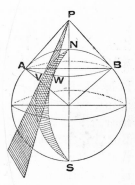

In fig. 41 PAB is a cone touching
he globe along the line AVWB. If

FIG. 41. — D i a g r a m
illustrating the
Constant of a Cone.

he apex of the cone be on the prolongation of the
xis of the globe, then AB is a parallel of latitude.
uppose NVS and NWS are any two meridians on
he globe, making an angle VNW at the North Pole.

[1] If, again, we imagine a light at the centre of the globe, the meridians
nd parallels will be projected in a manner similar to that just described
1 the cylindrical case. But here again a simple perspective projection
rould be of little use, because, as shown in the diagram (fig. 43), the
pacing of the parallels away from the parallel along which the cone
ouches the globe increases too rapidly. The meridians, however, would
e correctly spaced along the tangent parallel.

This angle on the globe corresponds to the angle VPW on the cone.

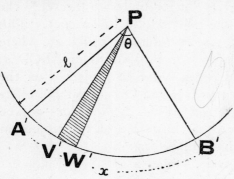

If we develop the cone PAB, we have a sector of a circle, PA'B' (fig. 42), in which the curve A'V'W'B' is of the same length as the parallel AVWB on the globe, and PA' is equal to PA.

FIG. 42.—Diagram illustrating the Constant of a Cone.

At the North Pole of the globe, the point of intersection of all meridians, there are four right angles. But in the sector A'PB' these four right angles are represented by the angle A'PB'. Similarly the angle VNW—an angle between any two meridians on the globe — is represented by the angle V'PW'.

As the four right angles at the pole are now "reduced" to

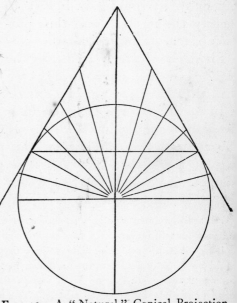

FIG. 43.—A "Natural" Conical Projection.

he angle A'PB', it follows that on the sector (i.e. he projection) the meridians are no longer at their rue angular distance apart, this distance having been educed. But all the angles made by the meridians it the poles have been reduced similarly, so that the ingle V'PW' bears the same proportion to the angle /NW as the whole angle A'PB' does to four right angles.

It is this proportion we imply in speaking of the constant of the cone, and so we can define the constant of the cone as the ratio that the whole angle of the cone, *when developed*, bears to four right angles.

Let us consider the constant of the cone in rather more detail. We can find its value quite simply in any particular case if we know two things :

(1) The length of the circle along which the cone touches the globe, and

(2) The slant length of the cone.

We have, then, a simple case of circular measure, for f we call the length of the base of the cone when developed

x, and the slant length of the cone l, we have $\theta = \dfrac{x}{l}$,

where θ is the angle at the apex of the cone when developed (the angle A'PB' in fig. 42).

The cone can be made to " open " or " close " : if we open it so as to make the apical angle, when developed, bigger and bigger, this angle will eventually become equal to 360 degrees because the cone has " opened out " into a plane. We have obtained one of the limiting cases—the cone has disappeared and we have a plane instead. In doing this it will be noticed that the cone has,[1] as it were, moved northwards, until finally, when it became tangent to the North Pole, it ceased

[1] I.e. the circle of contact has moved northwards.

to be a cone but became a plane. In fact, the greater the apical angle becomes, the higher the latitude to which the cone is tangent (see fig. 44).

Conversely, if we close the cone it becomes tangent to lower and lower parallels, until, finally, when the Equator is reached, the cone again disappears and this time passes into a cylinder—the second limiting case.

When the cone was opened out so that it passed into

a plane, the apical angle when developed became 360 degrees; the meridians on this plane would be spaced at their proper angular distances apart as on any of the zenithal projections. In other words, the ratio of the apical angle to 360 degrees is, in this case, as the ratio of 1 to 1.

FIG. 44.—Plane, Cone, and Cylinder.

But as we closed the cone the angle became smaller until finally in the other limiting case it disappeared or became 0 degrees. The ratio of 0 degrees to 360 degrees is as the ratio of 0 to 1. Thus we can say that the value of the constant of the cone varies between 0 and 1

Now let us examine the circle along which the cone touches the globe. Obviously a cone can touch a globe along any small circle, but it will be convenient if such

THE CONSTANT OF THE CONE

a circle is a parallel of latitude. If this be the case, as in the Simple Conical Projection with one Standard Parallel, the pole of the cone will lie on the prolongation of the Earth's axis.

When the cone is developed, the arc of the sector will be the same length as the parallel to which it was tangent on the globe. In other words, the scale of the arc on the sector, or projection, and the scale of the parallel on the globe are the same. Such a parallel is in the case of the Simple Conical Projection with one Standard Parallel called a Standard Parallel.

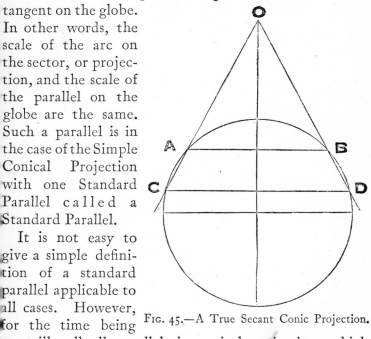

FIG. 45.—A True Secant Conic Projection.

It is not easy to give a simple definition of a standard parallel applicable to all cases. However, for the time being we will call all parallels in conical projections which are true to scale Standard Parallels. This definition is, perhaps, too comprehensive, because the one criterion here considered is that the parallel must be true to scale, the question of the actual method by which it is constructed not being taken into account at all. The interdependence of these criteria is shown in the account of Bonne's Projection.

But the student must not imagine that all standard parallels are parallels along which a cone is tangent to the sphere. If we have two standard parallels, it is manifestly impossible for the cone to be tangent to the sphere along both of them. The cone OCD in fig. 45 cuts the sphere along AB and CD, and we could make a projection on this cone. In actual fact such a projection would be a true Secant Conic Projection—not the Conic with two Standard Parallels (see page 78). However, this Secant Conic is never used. We may, nevertheless, make two standard parallels correct to scale and at the same time maintain an ordinary cone, although not a cone which is to be regarded as in any way touching or cutting the globe, but one that is entirely independent of it.

CHAPTER VIII

PART 1. CONICAL PROJECTIONS

THIS group includes a large number of projections, several of which are in common use in atlases. The modifications which may be made are similar to those which are made in the cases of the zenithals and the cylindricals. There are both equal-area conicals and orthomorphic conicals as well as simple forms. All of them are very easy to draw, and, as a class, they are suited to maps of countries in temperate latitudes which have not too great an extent in latitude.

THE SIMPLE CONIC PROJECTION WITH ONE STANDARD PARALLEL

As already explained, if a cone be placed over a sphere, it will touch it along one line. In the simple conic the pole of the cone is vertically above the pole of the globe and thus the two coincide (i.e. the globe and the cone) along a parallel of latitude. This is the standard parallel, and is divided truly. A central meridian is drawn to represent the meridian which actually runs through the centre of the country to be mapped. The parallels are spaced along it at their true distances apart, reduction being made for scale.

The standard parallel is first chosen. This parallel is made true to scale. In fig. 46 let A be a point on the sphere of latitude ϕ. Its co-latitude is the angle AON or χ. The radius required to draw the standard parallel

71

on the projection is AP, and in terms of the radius of the globe and the latitude, AP = R cot ϕ, because the angle APO = the angle AOE. The actual radius of the parallel of latitude on the sphere is AB, and AB = R cos ϕ, because the angle OAB = the angle AOE.

Thus the length of the parallel of which AB is the radius is 2πR cos ϕ. Any part of its length may be found, e.g. $1°$ of arc = $\dfrac{2\pi\text{R cos }\phi}{360}$, or $10°$ of arc = $\dfrac{2\pi\text{R cos }\phi}{36}$, and so on.

The constant of the cone is the proportion which the angle at the apex of the cone, when developed, bears to 360°. It is easy to show that the value of the constant is equal to the sine of the latitude of the standard parallel.

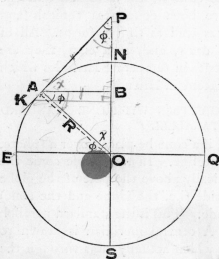

FIG. 46.—The Simple Trigonometry of the Simple Conic Projection.

In fig. 46

PA = R cot ϕ.

AB = R cos ϕ.

∴ length of parallel of which AB is radius = 2πR cos ϕ,

and the length of the circle of which PA is radius = 2πR cot ϕ.

Hence, n, the constant of the cone = $\dfrac{2\pi\text{R cos }\phi}{2\pi\text{R cot }\phi}$.

= $\dfrac{\cos \phi}{\cot \phi}$ = $\sin \phi$.

72

CONICAL PROJECTIONS

In fig. 46 let K represent the position of any other parallel on the projection of latitude ϕ_1. Its radius—on the projection—is PK. Its length on the projection is therefore $2\pi PK$ times the constant of the cone. But the true length of such a parallel on the sphere is $2\pi R \cos \phi_1$. Thus by finding the difference between the length on the projection and the length on the sphere the exaggeration is known, and the error per cent. can at once be obtained by multiplying the exaggeration, or difference, by 100 and dividing it by the true length of the parallel on the sphere.

For example : Length of parallel on the projection is $2PK\pi$ times the constant of the cone : the actual length is $2\pi R \cos \phi_1$; the difference is $2PK\pi \times$ constant $- 2\pi R \cos \phi_1$. The error per cent. is $d \times 100/2\pi R \cos \phi_1$, where d is the difference.

At present the length PK is not known, but if, as in the simple conic, divisions from A along PA are made at the actual distances apart of the parallels on the globe, AK will be equal to R times the difference of latitude of A and K expressed in circular measure. In other words, if the parallels are 10° apart, $AK = 2\pi R/36$ and $PK = PA + AK$.

In all true conical projections the meridians are straight lines and the parallels arcs of circles.

Simple Conic : Approximate Graphical Construction

Describe a circle representing the globe on the required scale. Choose the standard parallel, which may be drawn in by means of a protractor. Draw also the equator and the polar axis, which latter should be produced. From the point where the radius of the

73

standard parallel cuts the circle draw a tangent, producing it to meet the polar axis in P (fig. 47).

With radius PK describe the standard parallel. Then take any line (PM in fig. 48) as the central meridian. The parallels are spaced correctly—$2\pi R/360$ units apart to 1°. From the point where the standard parallel and the central meridian intersect one another, mark

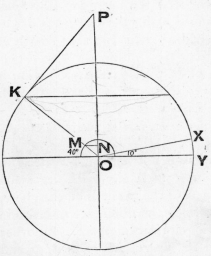

off the required divisions upwards and downwards.

To obtain the divisions on the standard parallel, construct as on the first diagram (fig. 47) an angle of 10°. With radius XY describe an arc with centre O. The divisions along the standard parallel are now given by the line MN, which is perpendicular to the polar axis and parallel to the Equator. Having

FIG. 47.—Graphical Construction of the Simple Conic Projection.

marked off these divisions along the standard parallel draw in the other meridians as straight lines, by joining these points to P. The other parallels are drawn as concentric circles with centre P and radii equal to PV PW, and so on (fig. 48).

[N.B.—The divisions along the central meridian are approximately equal to XY, and can be marked off accordingly, working outwards from M.]

This approximate method is, as a matter of fact

very nearly accurate. The error lies in assuming that the distance XY is a straight line rather than an arc of a circle. In small scales this matters little. In the same way MN is not really the true distance apart of the meridians on the standard parallel. However, if the spacing of the meridians and parallels were at 1° rather

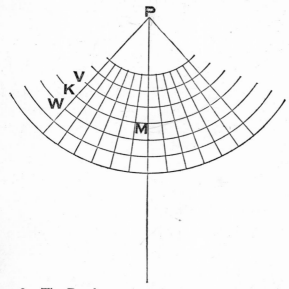

Fig. 48.—The Development of the Simple Conic Projection.

han at 10°, the errors would be much reduced assuming iccurate drawing, because the distance XY would thus, or all practical purposes, be the same for the arc as for he straight line. Similarly MN would be brought more iearly to exactitude.

TRIGONOMETRICAL CONSTRUCTION

In fig. 49a let ϕ be the latitude of A.

The radius required to draw the parallel A on the projection is AP. But AP = R cot ϕ.

The actual length of lat. A is $2\pi R \cos \phi$. If we require the meridians and parallels to be spaced at 10°, then an interval of 10° along the standard parallel is found by dividing its total length by 36;

$$\frac{2\pi R \cos \phi}{36}.$$

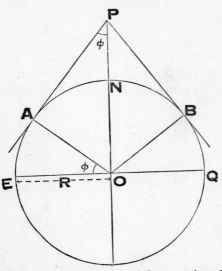

FIG. 49a.—Trigonometrical Construction of the Simple Conic Projection.

Mark off these distances along the standard parallel, commencing from A' and working outwards. Join these points by straight lines to P'. To obtain the parallels, divide the central meridian P'A' correctly, i.e. $2\pi R/36$, and mark off these divisions, again working outwards from A'. Then with centre P' describe arcs of circles passing through these points (fig. 49b).

It will be noticed that the pole of the Earth

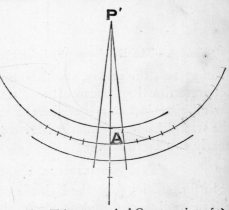

FIG. 49b.—Trigonometrical Construction of the Simple Conic Projection.

does not coincide with P′, because AP or A′P′ is longer than the arc AN ; in other words, the poles of the Earth and of the cone do not coincide.

By construction the scale is correct on the standard parallel and along the central meridian, and, because the other meridians are radii of a series of concentric circles, the scale along them is correct also. The scale along the other parallels is too great.

The projection is very simple to make and is much used for small countries which have no great extent in latitude. In atlases it is practically indistinguishable from the conic with two standard parallels; but as a general rule it may be assumed that, whereas small countries such as Ireland and Denmark are possibly shown on the simple conic, larger areas, such as Russia, Scandinavia, or even Europe are portrayed on the conic with two standard parallels.

Example.—Construction of a simple conic projection.

A map of the British Isles : scale, 1/1,000,000.

Standard parallel, 54° N.

Central meridian, 4° W.

Radius of the Earth assumed 250,000,000″.

Length of 1° of longitude on the standard parallel :

$$\frac{\pi R \cos lat.}{360} \times \frac{1}{M} = \frac{2 \times 3\cdot1416 \times 250,000,000 \times 0\cdot5878}{360 \times 1,000,000}$$

$$Scale = 2''\cdot56.$$

Length of 1° of latitude on the central meridian :

$$\frac{\pi R}{360} \times \frac{1}{M} = \frac{2 \times 3\cdot1416 \times 250,000,000}{360 \times 1,000,000} = 4''\cdot36 \text{ (approximately).}$$

Radius required to draw the standard parallel on the projection :—(*Vide* Ch. IX.)

$$R \cot lat. \times \frac{1}{M} = \frac{250,000,000 \times 0\cdot7265}{1,000,000} = 181''\cdot625.$$

PART 2. THE CONICAL WITH TWO STANDARD PARALLELS

In the case just described, only one parallel was made correct to scale. If, by slight modifications, we can have two parallels correct to scale as well as all the meridians, we have made a distinct advance, and have obtained a projection which is capable of very wide application.

Any two parallels may be chosen as standards. Naturally they will vary according to the map. Their choice, however, depends on the most economic distribution of error for the whole map. For example, if we need a map of Europe on this projection, we should not choose the 70th and 35th parallels of N. lat., but more probably the 60th and 40th of N. lat., because the continent is, as it were, more equally spaced about the two latter than the two former. Again, the more important parts of Europe lie within, or very near to, these two parallels and, other things being equal, these parts will need to be more exactly represented. If, on the other hand 70° and 35° N. were chosen, the central parts of Europe would suffer most—clearly a disadvantage.[1]

This projection has often been called the Secant Conic. Such a term is very misleading. A secant of a circle is any straight line cutting the circumference at two points. If we were to make a true Secant Conic Projection we should, therefore, make the distance between the standard parallels equal to the secant distance between them. As it is, we make use of the arc distance, so that the parallels are the same distance apart on the projection as on the globe, reduction being made for scale (see fig. 45).

[1] "In general it will be found sufficient to take the standard parallel about one-seventh of the whole extent in latitude from the bounding parallels" (Hinks).

TWO STANDARD PARALLELS

Approximate Construction of the Simple Conic with Two Standard Parallels

As in the ordinary simple conic, the meridians are radii and the parallels concentric circles. The problem we have is to find the radii of the two standard parallels. Having done this, we may proceed in a somewhat similar manner as in the Simple Conic.

First, draw any straight line, NM (fig. 50), and on it mark two points A and B. The distance AB is the correct distance apart of the two parallels chosen as standards, measured along the curve of the globe, $= 2\pi Rd$, where d is the difference in latitude, expressed as a fraction of the entire circumference. From A and B draw AA′ and BB′ perp. to NM. These two lines are made equal to a given length (say 10°) along the parallels A and B. If A = 70°, and B = 30° N,

then $AB = \dfrac{2\pi R}{9}$ (because $70° - 30°$

$= 40° = 1/9$ of 360°), and

$$AA' = \frac{2\pi R \cos 70°}{36}$$

$$\text{and } BB' = \frac{2\pi R \cos 30°}{36}.$$

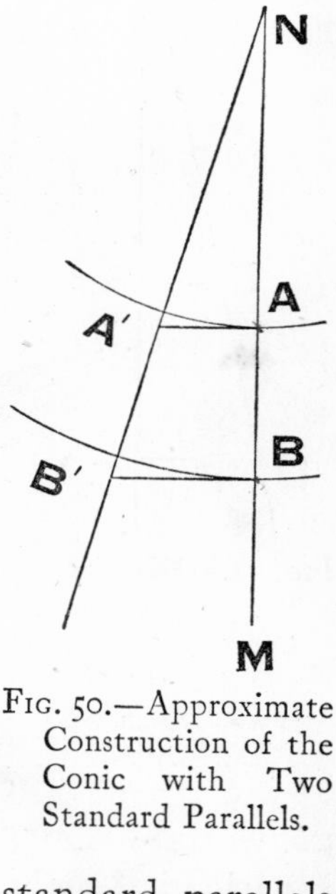

Fig. 50.—Approximate Construction of the Conic with Two Standard Parallels.

Join B′A′ and produce it to meet MN in N. The radii for the two standard parallels are then NA and NB, and the other parallels are found by dividing AB into as many parts as required, and continuing these divisions outwards towards N and M. For example, if we, as assumed, make intervals of latitude and longitude of 10°, then we must divide AB into four equal parts.

The meridians are then drawn in as in the simple conic with one standard parallel.

TRIGONOMETRICAL CONSTRUCTION

In fig. 51 let AC represent the Earth's axis prolonged and let EB and DC be the actual radii of the parallels o

latitude E and D respectively. Suppose ED to be the true distance apart of the two parallels (i.e. the arc distance here shown as a straight line). Join DE and produce it to A, then AE : AD :: EB DC, or AE : ED :: EB : DF.

Then the radii AE and AD will be proportional to the cosines of latitude E and D respectively.

To construct the projection, draw central meridian; with radii AE and AD draw the standard parallels and divide them correctly $\left(\dfrac{2\pi R \cos \text{lat.}}{360}\right)$. T

obtain the other parallels, divide ED correctly (i.e. if E = 70° and D = 40° and the map is to show parallels a intervals of 10°, divide ED into thre equal parts), and carry on these division

FIG. 51.—Diagram illustrating the Construction of the Conic with Two Standard Parallels.

above and below the standard parallels. Then draw con centric circles through all these points with A as centre

By construction, the scale along all meridians is correc and also along two parallels. The latitude scale be tween the standard parallels is too small, and outsid them it is too great. Thus, it is by judicious choic f the standard parallels that the errors of scale of the hole map may be minimised. It is a very valuable rojection; its greatest merit is that, combined with ie advantages already noticed, it is very easy to draw. : should not be used for countries having too great an xtent in latitude, but is suitable for any extent in ongitude. In atlases it often figures in maps of Europe, ussia, Scandinavia, etc. Asia is too big for it.

It is neither orthomorphic nor equal-area, but as the ieridians and the parallels are at right angles to one iother, it is more nearly orthomorphic than Bonne's, id the fact that this latter is equal-area is often more ian outweighed by other considerations.

Calculation of an Example

A map of part of the N. Atlantic on a scale of '50,000,000. Long. and lat. at intervals of 10°. Standard arallels, 40° N. and 70° N. Central meridian, 30° W.

By formula (see fig. 51) AE : ED :: EB : DF.

ED is the actual distance apart of the parallels, or πR/12.

EB = R cos 70° = 5 × 0·3420 = 1·7100 inches.

DF = DC − EB = R cos 40° − R cos 70° = 3·8300 − 1·7100 = 2·1200 inches.

$$AE = \frac{2·618 \times 1·71}{2·12} = 2·112 \text{ inches.}$$

And DA = 2·112 + 2·618 = 4·730 inches.

Distance apart of the meridians on lat. 40°

$$= \frac{R \cos 40 \times 2\pi}{36} = 0·6685.$$

Distance apart of the parallels on the central meridian

$$= \frac{2·618}{3} = 0·8726.$$

The construction of this projection may be approache in rather a different way.

Choose two parallels, ϕ_1 and ϕ_2, as standards.

Our problem is to obtain their radii, SA_1 and SA_2, o *the projection* (fig. 51A).

The standard parallels are to be their true length– $2\pi R \cos \phi_1$ and $2\pi R \cos \phi_2$.

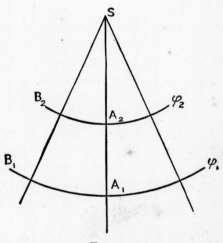

Fig. 51A.

Further, the parallels are to be correctly spaced on tl meridians, and thus $A_2A_1 = \dfrac{2\pi R}{360} \times (\phi_1 - \phi_2)$.

The sectors SA_1B_1 and SA_2B_2 are exactly similar c the projection,

hence $SA_1 : SA_2 : : A_1B_1 : A_2B_2$

but $SA_1 : SA_2 : : \cos \phi_1 : \cos \phi_2$

$\therefore \quad SA_1 = \dfrac{SA_2 \cos \phi_1}{\cos \phi_2}$

and $SA_1 - SA_2 = A_1A_2 = \dfrac{2\pi R}{360} (\phi_1 - \phi_2)$

Substituting for SA_1

we have $\dfrac{SA_2 \cos \phi_1}{\cos \phi_2} - SA_2 = \dfrac{2\pi R}{360} (\phi_1 - \phi_2)$

$\therefore \quad \dfrac{SA_2 (\cos \phi_1 - \cos \phi_2)}{\cos \phi_2} = \dfrac{2\pi R}{360°} (\phi_1 - \phi_2)$

and $SA_2 = \dfrac{2\pi R}{360°} (\phi_1 - \phi_2) \dfrac{\cos \phi_2}{(\cos \phi_1 - \cos \phi_2)}$

This gives us the radius of the parallel ϕ_2. Since the parallels are to be spaced at their true distances apart, we can find the radius of any other parallel.

Suppose the parallels are to be 10° apart, then the radii of the parallels on either side of ϕ_2 will be :

$$SA_2 \pm \dfrac{2\pi R}{36°}$$

(On page 81 an example was worked out for the North Atlantic Ocean.

Using this alternative method, the radius AE (page 81) would be given by the equation :

$$SA_2 = \dfrac{2\pi R}{360°} (\phi_1 - \phi_2) \dfrac{\cos \phi_2}{(\cos \phi_1 - \cos \phi_2)}$$

$$= \dfrac{2 \times 3 \cdot 1416 \times 5}{360} (40° N - 70° N) \dfrac{0 \cdot 3420}{0 \cdot 7660 - 0 \cdot 3420}$$

$$= \dfrac{2 \times 3 \cdot 1416 \times 5}{12} \times \dfrac{0 \cdot 3420}{0 \cdot 4240}$$

$$= 2 \cdot 111 \text{ inches)}$$

PART 3. THE POLYCONIC PROJECTION (A MODIFIED CONICAL PROJECTION)

Here again the construction is, at root, the same as in Bonne's and in the simple conic. However, the parallels are no longer concentric circles, each being constructed with its own particular centre and radius. The central meridian is divided as in the simple conic, the parallels as in Bonne.

GRAPHICAL CONSTRUCTION

Make a circle to scale to represent the globe (fig. 52).

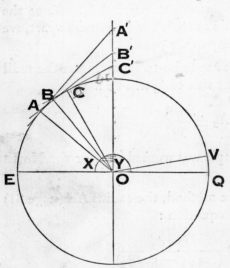

For as many degrees of latitude as necessary set off angles with a protractor. Then at A, B, C, and other such points draw tangents AA', BB', CC', etc. If the meridians and parallels are to be 10° apart, set off an angle VOQ of 10°. With radius VQ describe an arc with centre O. Then draw perpendiculars such as XY for each degree of latitude.

FIG. 52.—Graphical Construction of the Polyconic Projection.

To make the projection, draw any central line (fig. 53). Space it by means of dividers into intervals equal to VQ. To draw the parallels, first number the divisions on the perpendicular (i.e. the central meridian)

THE POLYCONIC PROJECTION

and then with radii AA′, BB′, CC′, etc., describe arcs [1] passing through those points on the central meridian— i.e. if A = 40°, then AA′ must be an arc passing through the 40° mark on the central meridian, and so on. The circles are not concentric. Then divide each parallel correctly by taking off with dividers the distance XY, etc., commencing from the central meridian and working outwards. Finally, join corresponding points on each parallel by curves which are the meridians.

TRIGONOMETRICAL CONSTRUCTION

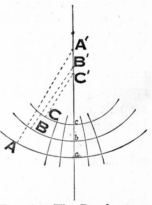

FIG. 53.—The Development of the Polyconic Projection.

In fig. 52 (page 84) the radii for the drawing of the parallels, A, B, C, are respectively AA′, BB′, CC′—in each case R times the cotangent of the latitude of A, B, and C. Divide, first, the central meridian—$2\pi Rd$* (the scale being 1/250,000,000) marking off these divisions at their correct interval, not, however, commencing in any particular place. Let a, b, c be these divisions on fig 53. Now through a, b, c draw circles with radii AA′, BB′, CC′ respectively. It will be seen that the circles with greatest radius are those for lower latitudes. Then divide each parallel correctly—$\dfrac{2\pi R \cos \text{lat.}}{36}$ to 10°. The meridians are then drawn as in Bonne (q.v.).

[1] The centres of these arcs are on the central meridian or its prolongation.

* d = Required interval of latitude expressed as a fraction of the whole circumference of the globe.

The scale is true along the central meridian and along all the parallels. But because these are no longer concentric circles, the equal-area property has disappeared (see page 91). The meridian scale increases rapidly away from the central meridian. It is even less orthomorphic than Bonne on account of the rapidly increasing meridian scale. These two disadvantages render it useless for large areas on a single sheet. It is very useful for topographical maps, and a modified form is used for the One-in-a-Million Map.

Corresponding meridians on either side of the central meridian are divided similarly, and because all parallels are true it follows that separate sheets of a topographical map fit exactly along their north and south edges and have a rolling fit along their east and west edges.

" Its value lies in the fact that a general table can be calculated for the polyconic which depends only on the values for the size and shape of the earth. For the radius of each parallel depends only on its latitude, and not in the least upon the position of the centre or the extent of the map " (Hinks).

Thus for topographical maps its main advantages are :

1. By means of tables each sheet may be plotted independently.

2. The practical fit of adjacent sheets.

It is not possible to join a large number of sheets together to make a large map.

PART. 4 BONNE'S (MODIFIED) CONICAL PROJECTION

The general construction is very similar to that of the simple conic with one standard parallel. In Bonne all parallels are true to scale, and in this sense they are ıll standard parallels. But in the simple conic and the polyconic the standard parallels are all constructed on a definite radius—R × cotangent of the latitude. This is not the case in Bonne, only one parallel being so constructed, the others being drawn as concentric circles, with radii found by marking off divisions correct to scale on the central meridian.

However, the curvature of all the parallels depends

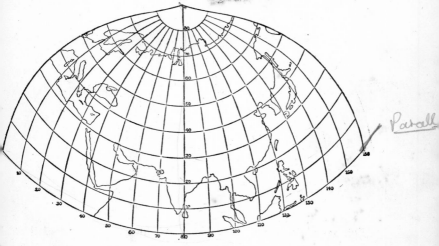

Fɪɢ. 54.—Asia on a Bonne's Projection with selected Standard Parallel 80° N.

on that one selected for construction with a radius equal to the cotangent of the latitude. The importance of this can be appreciated best by consideration of an actual case. Suppose we were to map Asia on a Bonne's projection. We have to choose one parallel which we are to construct with a radius of R times the cotangent of the latitude. Suppose we choose 80° N. (fig. 54). The cotangent of 80°—on the adopted scale—will give us a very short radius, and, as all the parallels in Bonne are concentric circles, they will all conform to the curvature of this selected parallel. If this parallel were 80° N., the radii of all the parallels would be so short as badly to distort, or rather "to compress," the shape of the map. If, on the other hand, we selected 40° N. as standard (fig. 55), we should have a greater radius at the

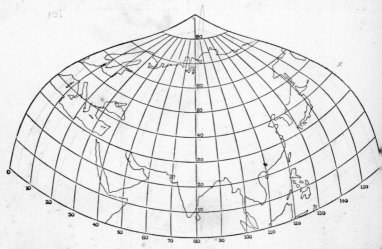

FIG. 55.—Asia on a Bonne's Projection with selected Standard Parallel for 40° N.

commencement, and, as all the other parallels would be conformable, the resulting map would be less "cramped."

The two figures show graticules both on a scale of *c.* 1/160,000,000, the one being controlled by a selected parallel of 80° N., the other by 40° N.

The parallel selected to govern the curvature of all the other parallels will vary in different cases. In general we may say that the nearer the main mass of a country is to the Equator, the lower the selected parallel ; and conversely, the nearer a country is to the Poles, the higher the parallel.[1]

Bonne's projection is much used in atlases for maps of Europe, Asia, North America, South America, Australia, and other large areas. If such areas have not a great extent in latitude and longitude it is very suitable ; but on account of the increasing obliquity of the meridians to the parallels towards the edges of the map, shape is much distorted. Thus it is that Asia is not so well shown on Bonne as on the zenithal equal-area. (Cf. figs. 54 and 55 and Plate VIII.).

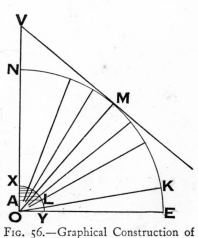

FIG. 56.—Graphical Construction of Bonne's Projection.

GRAPHICAL CONSTRUCTION

In fig. 56 let NME represent a quadrant of the Earth to scale. If the meridians and parallels are to be 10° apart, lay off, as in the simple conic, OK, making an angle of 10° with OE. With radius KE, describe the arc XLY. Having chosen the standard parallel for the map and having laid it off with a protractor, and as many other parallels as necessary, draw lines such as AL parallel to OE. Then with radius VM describe an arc ;

[1] It will be seen later that in approaching the Equator we are nearing one of the limiting cases of Bonne—namely the Sinusoidal. On the other hand, in approaching polar areas we are passing toward Werner's Projection—which is an ordinary Bonne with the Pole as the selected standard parallel.

divide this truly, working outwards from the central meridian. (In the figs. 56 and 57, 50° N. is the standard parallel.) Then divide the central meridian truly, working outwards from M' (the divisions are equal to KE). Through all such points draw concentric circles, with the centre V'. Now divide each parallel truly, making use of such divisions as AL, etc. The meridians are

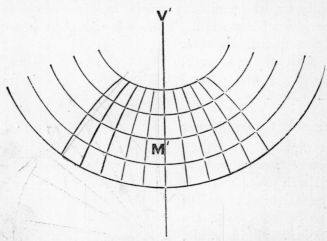

Fig. 57.—Development of Bonne's Projection.

then drawn through similar points on each parallel (fig. 57).

Trigonometrical Construction

Choose a parallel to give a curvature suitable to the country to be mapped ; and construct it with radius of R times the cotangent of the latitude. The central meridian is a straight line and is divided as in the simple conic ($2\pi Rd$).[1] The other parallels are concentric with

[1] $d =$ interval of latitude or longitude expressed as a fraction of the circumference of the globe.

ne standard parallel and are passed through the points
lready obtained on the central meridian. Each parallel,
ncluding that selected to govern the curvature of all,
 then treated as if it were a standard parallel and is
ivided correctly ($2\pi R \cos$ lat. d) (see footnote, p. 90) ;
ne other meridians are obtained by passing smooth
urves through corresponding points on the parallels.

The projection is an equal-area projection. Consider
small part of it (fig. 58). The perpendicular distance

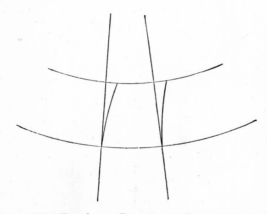

FIG. 58.—The Equal-area Property of Bonne's Projection.

etween parallels is correct (they are concentric circles)
nd the parallels themselves are true to scale. In fact,
he rectangle enclosed by any two parallels and meridians
n the globe has been made equal to a parallelogram on
he projection which is on an equal base and of equal
eight to scale.

Example.—Calculations required for a map of Asia,
n a scale of 1/25,000,000 (R = 10″).
Ieridians and parallels at intervals of 10°,

Selected standard parallel $= 45°$ N. lat.

Radius of standard parallel on projection $= R \cot 45°$

$= 10''.$

Intervals of 10° of lat. on C.M. $= 2\pi R/36$

$= 1''\!\cdot\!7453.$

Intervals of 10° of lat. on S.P. $= \dfrac{2\pi R \cos 45°}{36}$

$= 1''\!\cdot\!2330.$

Intervals of 10° on any other parallel $= \dfrac{2\pi R \cos \text{lat}}{36}$

e.g. 70° N. $= \dfrac{2\pi R \cos 70°}{36}$

$= 0''\!\cdot\!5969,$

and so on.

CHAPTER IX

ONSTRUCTION OF THE CONICAL PROJECTIONS BY MEANS OF RECTANGULAR CO-ORDINATES

ᴏʀ maps on a large scale it is inconvenient, and often mpossible, to draw the parallels directly, because their dii are so great. However, the co-ordinate method is ot difficult and tables giving co-ordinates are available. he principle does not involve more than simple trigo-

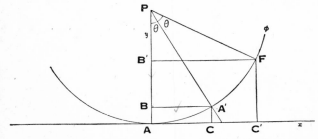

Fɪɢ. 59.—The Rectangular Co-ordinates of the Conic Projections.

ometry; but if tables are not at hand, it is tedious work out the co-ordinates of all points.

The central meridian is taken as one axis; the other a tangent to the parallel in question where it crosses e central meridian. In fig. 59 let P be the apex of e cone; AA′ part of the standard parallel of latitude ϕ. A (or PA′) is the radius required to draw the standard arallel. PA is the central meridian. To plot the oint A′ we must know the lengths of BA′ and CA′—

93

STUDY OF MAP PROJECTIONS

the x and y co-ordinates of the point respectively. The angle APA′ must also be known.

Having found these values, we can see that

BA′ = PA′ sin θ = r sin θ.

PB = PA′ cos θ = r cos θ.

But AB = PA − PB = r − r cos θ.

In other words, the co-ordinates of the point A are, $x = r$ sin θ.

$y = r - r$ cos θ.

The value of θ is found as follows :

Let AA′ be an arc of 10° of longitude along an parallel, i.e. AA′ $= \dfrac{2\pi R \cos \phi}{36}$.

Then θ in circular measure $= \dfrac{\text{arc AA}′}{\text{PA}} = \dfrac{\frac{2\pi R \cos}{36}}{\text{PA}}$

Calculation of an Example.—Simple conical projection on a scale of 1/5,000,000 (R = 50″). 45° N. is the standard parallel.

Then $r = 50″$ cot 45° = 50 × 1·000 = 50·000.

AA′ $= \dfrac{2\pi R \cos 45°}{36} = 6″·170$.

Then by circular measure $\theta = \dfrac{\text{AA}′}{\text{PA}} = \dfrac{6·170}{50} = 0·123$ radians, or 7° 3′.

And $x = r$ sin θ = 50 × 0·1228 = 6″·14

$y = r - r$ cos θ = 50 − 50 × 0·9924

= 50 − 49·62 = 0″·38.

The distances are all found in the same way, and all that is necessary is to find the value of θ. For example the co-ordinates of a point 10° E. of A′, and on the same parallel, are found directly by doubling the value of θ. As all conical projections are symmetrical about

heir central meridian, the corresponding points on the
ther side are plotted at once.

To plot the other parallels, their radii on the projec-
ion must first be found, and then the co-ordinates are
alculated as before. For example : The radius of 60° N.
s (on the simple conical) R cot (lat. of the standard
arallel) minus $2\pi Rd$, where d is the difference in latitude

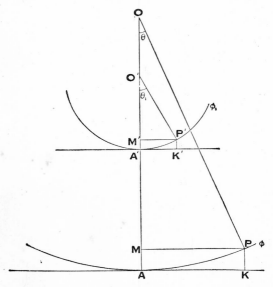

ɪɢ. 60.—The Construction of the Polyconic by means of Rectangular
Co-ordinates.

etween the standard parallel and the one in question,
xpressed as a fraction of the globe's circumference.
Iaving obtained the necessary points along two parallels,
/hich are better if near the northern and southern borders
f the map, the meridians may be drawn in as straight
nes through corresponding points on each.

This holds good for all the conics which have straight

meridians and parallels which are arcs of concentri circles. The parallels are drawn through points on th central meridian, which is divided truly, and simila points on the other meridians, because all meridians ar clearly divided in the same manner.

In Bonne's projection, first plot the standard parall as in the simple conic. The other parallels are als plotted as before ; in this case, however, every parall must be plotted. Then each parallel is divided correctl and finally curves are drawn through these points t represent the meridians. In the case of the polyconi rather more constructional work is necessary. As eac parallel is plotted with its own particular radius, different set of co-ordinates must be worked out fo each parallel (fig. 60). The meridians are plotted a in Bonne.

CHAPTER X

PART 1. CYLINDRICAL PROJECTIONS

ROJECTIONS on a circumscribed cylinder are very
ommon in atlases. Most of these, however, are con-
entional or non-geometrical projections. If one were
o make a perspective cylindrical projection, the exaggera-
on would be very great indeed—in fact, the same
in a gnomonic. This is readily seen in the diagram
g. 40). The " natural " projections of A, B, C . . .
e A′, B′, C′. . . . It is clear that on such a projection
e Poles cannot be shown. The scale is correct only
a the Equator.

The cylinder need not touch the Equator; it may
circle the globe along any great circle. A transverse
ercator is constructed on this principle. However,
rectly some slight calculations are employed in the
uatorial case, useful modifications can be made: if
e area between any two lines of latitude is preserved
rrectly, we have the cylindrical equal-area; if the
aggeration of the longitude scale is made to increase
the same proportion as the latitude scale, we have the
ercator or cylindrical orthomorphic projection. These
e the two commonest types, but the simple cylindrical
which the true spacing of the parallels is maintained,
d the " carte parallélogrammatique " in which the
ale along two parallels is correct, have some slight theo-
tical interest. They are, in fact, the equivalents of

the simple conic and the conic with two standar
parallels.

PART 2. THE SIMPLE CYLINDRICAL PROJECTION OR PLATE CARRÉE

This is the cylindrical projection which correspond
to the simple conic and the zenithal equidistant. Th
meridians in each case are divided as on the globe, s
that the parallels are their correct distance apart. I
the simple cylindrical all that is necessary is to find th
length of a meridian, divide it correctly, and draw th
Equator at right angles to it and, of course, twice it
length. The other parallels are straight lines parall
to the Equator and of the same length as the Equato
The meridians are all straight lines perpendicular to th
Equator and spaced along it at their proper interval
Thus the graticule forms a series of squares.

Computation of an Example.—A simple cylindric
map of the World on a scale of 1/125,000,000. Clearl
$R = 2''$, and 10° of latitude or of longitude are equ
to $\frac{2\pi R}{36} = 0''\cdot349$ (fig. 61).

This projection is of very little use; it is neither equa
area nor orthomorphic. Further, the Poles are mac
the same size as the Equator, so that it has all the di
advantages without any of the advantages of the oth
cylindrical projections. The scale is true along all th
meridians and along the Equator.

PART 3. THE CYLINDRICAL EQUAL-AREA PROJECTION

In this projection, one of Lambert's, the meridia
and parallels are straight lines and perpendicular one
another. But the area between any two parallels

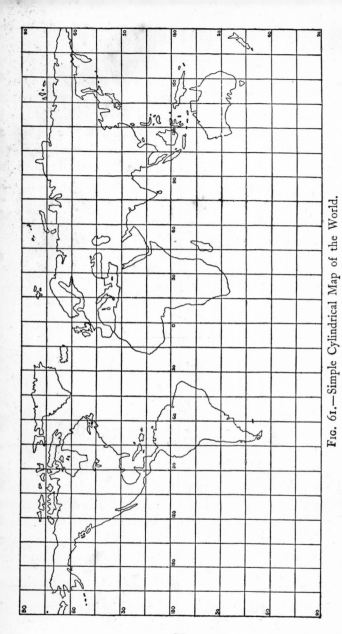

Fig. 61.—Simple Cylindrical Map of the World.

99

made equal to the corresponding area on the globe. It has been shown that the area of a zone on the sphere is equal to $2\pi Rh$, where h is the vertical distance between the parallels limiting the zone. If ϕ is the latitude of one of the limiting parallels of the zone and the Equator is the other, then $h = R \sin \phi$.

The Equator is made its true length to scale, and is divided as in the simple cylindrical. The Poles are again the same length as the Equator.

Computation of an Example.—A World map. Scale

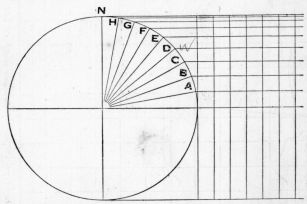

Fig. 62.—The Construction of the Cylindrical Equal-area Projection.

$1/250,000,000$ (R $= 1''$) (fig. 62). From the formula it can be seen that the spacing of the parallels is as the sines of the angles of latitude, i.e. $10°$ N. (or S.) is distant from the Equator R sin $10°$, or $0''\cdot1736$, lat. $20° = 0''\cdot3420$, and so on. The intervals between the parallels thus decrease away from the Equator. As the true spacing of the parallels on the globe $= \dfrac{2\pi R}{36}$, it is clear that the meridian scale is considerably reduced, but this is compensated by the exaggeration of the scale along the parallels. Thus on lat. $40°$ N., $10°$ of longitude $= \dfrac{2\pi R \cos 40°}{36} = 0''\cdot 1336$,

whereas on the projection the distance is the same as on the Equator.

In order, then, to preserve area the shape is greatly distorted, the compression in a north and south direction being balanced by an east and west exaggeration.

This projection is sometimes used for World maps to show distributions. It is not a very successful projection.

GRAPHICAL CONSTRUCTION

The cylindrical equal-area can be constructed very easily by graphical means. Draw to scale a circle to represent the globe, and with a protractor lay off angles at the required intervals of latitude (fig. 62).

Then through the points A, B, C, D, E, N draw lines parallel to the Equator. These are the parallels of latitude.

The meridians are spaced at equal distances ($2\pi Rd$) along the Equator as in the Plate Carrée, where d is the interval of longitude expressed as a fraction of the circumference of the globe.

PART 4. MERCATOR'S PROJECTION

This is probably the best known of all projections, because it is used for navigation purposes and also in nearly all atlases for maps of the world, and for wall-maps. Although it has certain great merits, it is largely responsible for many geographical misconceptions, e.g. the misleading appearance of the polar areas. These areas are greatly exaggerated when shown on this projection ; this great increase in north and south latitudes apparently extends the size of the Antarctic continent enormously in comparison with equatorial regions. Another well-known example of this anomaly is the comparison of Greenland with South America. In actual fact, Greenland is about one-tenth the size of South America, but on the projection it appears to be rather larger.

Although Mercator is actually best suited for sailing purposes, the sailing routes themselves are not very easily plotted on it, and difficulties are likely to arise unless the user of the map fully understands its limitations. On the projection all parallels are of the same length as the Equator, and consequently the latitude scale increases with increasing distance from the Equator. In fact, a separate scale line is necessary for each parallel. On the other hand, owing to the convergence of the meridians on the globe at the Poles, the shortest distance between any two points due east and west of one another and which are not on the Equator, is not along the parallel of latitude passing through them, it is to the north of that line in the northern hemisphere and to the south of it in the southern hemisphere.

The mathematical proof of this is not easy, but a practical and equally convincing proof can be obtained very simply. Take a large globe and choose any two places approximately in the same latitude. Stretch a piece of india-rubber band between them along their common parallel. Then, keeping the two ends of the rubber firm, shift the free middle part until it is least stretched.[1] It will be found that, if the observation

[1] A similar experiment may be made with string. Place a piece of string between two places approximately on the same parallel of latitude —e.g. San Francisco and Tokio—so that the string rests loosely along

re being made north of the Equator, the rubber is least
stretched when moved northwards, and vice versa in
the southern hemisphere. The same result will obtain
even if the places are not in the same latitude. It will
be found also that this shortest distance is an arc of a
circle, and that if the circle were completed it would
pass entirely round the globe—it would, in fact, be a
great circle. We are thus led to the conclusion that
the shortest distance between any two points on the
Earth's surface is along the (shorter arc of the) great
circle passing through them.

Unhappily, the great-circle course on a Mercator
projection is seldom a straight line. No great circle
on the globe, except the Equator or a meridian, will
cut meridians or parallels at constant angles. It is
this fact which renders the plotting of great circles on
Mercator a rather awkward matter.

Suppose we make a voyage from Southampton to
Rio de Janeiro. Ignoring the land masses, we should
find that, as a result of our experiments with india-
rubber on a globe, our course ran very nearly through
Madeira, the Cape Verdes, and Pernambuco. On the
other hand, if we were to sail from Lisbon to New York,
we should find that the shortest way was well to the
north of the parallel of 40° N. latitude, which nearly
passes through both places.

It is now necessary to examine this shortest course
on a Mercator map. Deferring the details of construc-
the common parallel. Hold one end of the string firm and draw the
string taut in such a way that it still passes through both places. The
free middle part of the string will move northwards. The experiment
could be made between places in the southern hemisphere, or between
places north and south of the Equator. In each case the course on the
globe marked out by the string, when drawn taut, is part of a great circle,

tion to a later paragraph, we may note here tha
meridians and parallels are straight lines at right angle
to one another, and that while the meridians are equi
distant, the parallels are spaced at intervals whicl
increase away from the Equator. This spacing of the
parallels is so arranged that at any point of intersection
of parallel and meridian (in practice any small area) the
scale in all directions is the same. In other words, the
projection is orthomorphic. Hence, as the meridian.
and the parallels are straight lines at right angles, any
straight line drawn in any direction on a Mercato
chart crosses all parallels at a constant angle, and also
all meridians at a constant angle. Such a line is called
a " rhumb line " or a " loxodrome." But as meridian:
all run true north and south on a Mercator chart, i
follows that a straight line crossing them must have a
constant bearing.[1]

This is the great merit of Mercator and the reasor
why it is used for purposes of navigation. A sailor, i
told to sail on a constant bearing, has but to plot thi
bearing on the chart and his course is found. Further
it is just as easy to sail along a series of such bearings
the angular points being defined by means of latitud
and longitude.

Now, it has been shown that the shortest distance
between any two places on the globe is along the arc o
the great circle passing through them. A little though
will show that to sail along a circular course other thar

---

[1] A straight line drawn between two places on any other cylindrica
projection cuts all meridians at the same angle, but it is not a loxodrome
It is due to the combination of equality of scale along parallel and meridian
and of meridians and parallels being at right angles to one another
which renders a straight line on a Mercator chart a line of *true* bearing.

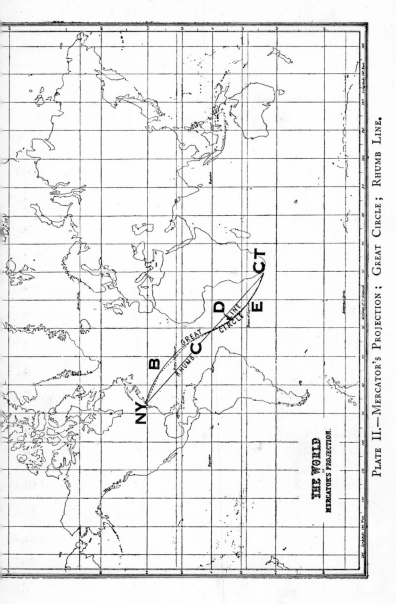

THE WORLD
MERCATOR'S PROJECTION.

Plate II.—Mercator's Projection; Great Circle; Rhumb Line.

105

the Equator or a meridian means that direction changes every moment—clearly a drawback in practical navigation. However, it is not difficult to combine great-circle principles with constant bearings or loxodromes. In theory a slight increase in distance must result, but not enough to make any serious difference. In Plate II let NY, BCDE, CT, be the great-circle course between NY and CT. If a series of chords be drawn, such as NY–B, B–C, C–D, D–E, we have four loxodromes, and the changes in the course may be made at B, C, D and E. It is obvious that the chord distance and the arc distance are not so divergent as to make the principle of no avail.

In actual practice another point comes in. Most great-circle courses are not possible by sea alone. The course, as plotted, may cut across land and sea in an impossible fashion. Consequently each separate "reach" by sea must be plotted independently and the final course is a summation of the several parts.

We are now in a position to compare the merits of a Mercator and of a gnomonic chart. On the former straight lines are lines of constant bearing; on the latter, their bearing is no longer constant, but they are actually the shortest distance between two points. At first sight it may seem that the latter advantage is of greater weight, but the excessive exaggeration of a gnomonic projection minimises the value of this property. In point of fact, it will be shown later that the Pole cannot be represented on Mercator, but this matters less because, other things being equal, polar areas are not likely to form an important part of the chart, at any rate from the point of view of practical navigation. On the other hand, the exaggeration in a gnomonic chart ncreases outwards in all directions, and at the same ate, from the centre of the map.

Again, it is impossible to map even a complete hemi phere on a gnomonic chart, whereas the whole World, with the exception of very high latitudes, can be shown n a Mercator map. Certainly this difficulty may be overcome to some extent by developing the gnomonic nap as on a circumscribed cube, but the calculations are ong and it is not very convenient to have to plot sailing courses over different faces of the cube.[1] In contrast o this, Mercator's projection is extremely simple to onstruct from tables—all that is necessary is to draw traight lines at their correct distances apart. Lastly, he fact that Mercator has come into such very wide se through navigation gives it an enormous pull over ny other—it has had the " momentum of a start."

Only the nature of the construction can be given here. The crux of the whole matter is so to space the parallels hat at any point the scale is the same along meridian nd parallel. Mercator is really one of the cylindrical rojections and may be found under the name of the " cylindrical orthomorphic."

The simplest way of realising the process is that given n Dr. Garnett's *Little Book on Map Projection*. If we ake a very narrow gore—i.e. a strip between two meri- ians on the globe—and spread it out flat, we have very early obtained an equal-area map of that strip, because f the gore is sufficiently narrow there will be no great istortion in spreading it out quite flat. On the other and, a wider gore would be considerably distorted. However, let us consider a narrow one. The length of he spread-out gore is half the circumference of the

[1] See p. 132.

globe, and, assuming no distortion, the parallel an
meridian scales are true. But if we are to make th
scale at 90° N. or S. equal to that at the Equator, w
must imagine the Pole stretched out in an east-wes
direction to the width of the gore at the Equator.

This is only half of the problem. Whilst stretchin
out the polar areas in this way, a similar stretching ha
also to be made in a north and south direction, so tha
if, for example, the length of the gore in 60° N. or S
lat. is doubled in an east and west direction, a ver
narrow strip of that gore in these latitudes is also double
in a north and south direction. The effect of th
double stretching is to render areas on the projectio
too great. Consider the strip on 60°: this parallel i
just half as long as the Equator, thus to make it of th
same length implies a doubling of the scale. At the sam
time the actual parallel itself (in practice a very narro
strip, not a line) must be doubled in a north an
south direction to keep it in direct proportion to th
meridian scale. Having thus increased both meridia
and parallel scale twice, the area is obviously quadruple

The farther one goes north or south the greater doe
the stretching become, so that areas increase enormously
In fact on parallel 75° areas are increased approximatel
fifteen times and at latitude 80° thirty-three time
Thus it is that near the Poles the stretching would b
so great that it is useless to show very high latitudes.

As at every point the stretching has been the same i
all directions, it follows that the shape of areas has bee
magnified but not distorted. If we had a small squar
at 40° N. or S. on the globe and we stretched it x time
in every direction, we should have a square still. Thu
the projection is orthomorphic. It is very important t

:alise the limits of orthomorphism. If any very small
:ea not on the Equator be considered, it is clear that,
n the projection, this small area has expanded. Similarly,
ny other small area will expand. But if we take two
ich areas not in the same latitude, the expansion of
ie one is greater or less than that of the other, and
ie scale for the one is unsuitable for the other.

Strictly speaking, then, orthomorphism is applicable
nly to points ; in practice it may be applied to very
mall areas. In this way we avoid an apparent paradox
—we have said that South America is nine or ten times
igger than Greenland, whereas on the projection
Greenland is bigger than South America. Yet it is
uite true to say that a tiny piece of Greenland is just
s correctly represented on Mercator as a correspondingly
iny piece of South America, in so far as shape is
oncerned.

A Means of Constructing Mercator's Projection

t is not easy to derive a general formula for the construction
f this projection. However, if each parallel of latitude be con-
dered separately, it is a simple matter to find the distance of a
rticular parallel from the Equator. It has been noted already
at the exaggeration in the latitude scale at any point is equal
that of the longitude scale. But the latitude scale is altered
such a way that it is kept equal to the scale along the Equator.
, then, we can find out how much any parallel has been in-
eased we have a means of finding the distance, on the projection,
f that parallel from the Equator.

As each parallel of latitude is of the same length as the Equator,
ie exaggeration of the latitude scale varies as the secant of the
titude :

Let x be the scale,

then $x = \dfrac{\text{Projection length of the parallel}}{\text{True length.}}$

$= \dfrac{2\pi R}{2\pi R \cos. \text{lat.}} = \dfrac{1}{\cos. \text{lat.}} = \text{sec. lat.}$

Thus a table of secants will show directly the amount of th exaggeration on any parallel. In order, however, to obtain th distance of the particular parallel from the Equator on the projec tion, the sum of the secants from the Equator to that paralle must be found, and the result multiplied by $\dfrac{\pi R}{180}$, where R the radius of the sphere to scale.

(N.B.—$\dfrac{2\pi R}{360}$ or $\dfrac{\pi R}{180}$ is the length of one degree of longitud on the Equator.)

CHAPTER XI

THE SANSON FLAMSTEED OR SINUSOIDAL PROJECTION

THIS is a particular case of Bonne's projection. The
Equator is taken as the standard parallel and is a straight
line true to scale; the central meridian is a straight line
perpendicular to the Equator, and half its length. The
central meridian is also divided truly. The parallels
are straight and equidistant and are all correctly spaced
for the meridians. The meridians are curves drawn
through corresponding points on the several parallels.
For the same reason as in the case of Bonne, the projection is an equal-area projection. The whole sphere can
be shown, though the shape is a little awkward. A
greater disadvantage is that towards the edges of the
map the meridians are very oblique to the parallels and
consequently the shape is much distorted. It is very
frequently used for maps of Africa, Oceania, South
America and sometimes for Australia. It is, however,
not very suitable for the last.

GRAPHICAL CONSTRUCTION

Make a circle to scale to represent the globe. Lay off
with a protractor angles corresponding to the desired
interval between the parallels and meridians (15° in
fig. 63). With radius MN describe an arc with centre O.
Then draw parallel lines for each angle such as KL.

STUDY OF MAP PROJECTIONS

Draw a line E'N' (fig. 64) to represent the Equator on the map. At a point O in this line drop a perpendicular POP'. Along POP' and E'N' mark off divisions equal to MN, because both Equator and central meridian are divided similarly. Through the points thus obtained on POP' draw parallel lines, which are in fact the lines of latitude. Along each of these lines—working outwards from the central meridian—mark off division such as KL, etc. To complete the projection, pass curves through these points on the parallels—these are the meridians.

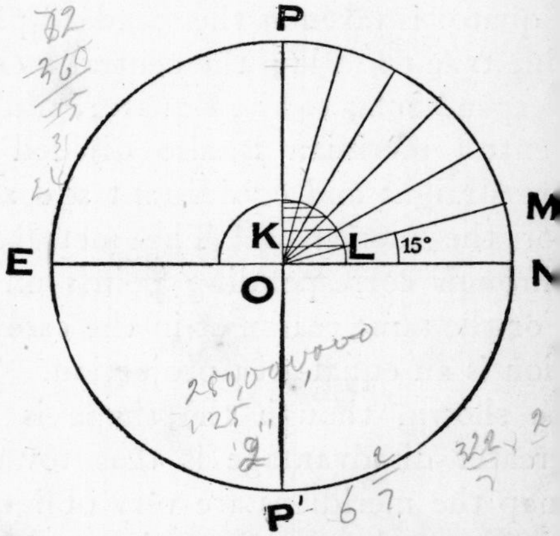

TRIGONOMETRICAL CONSTRUCTION

A development of the whole sphere on a scale of 1/125,000,000.

The length of the Equator is correct: $2\pi R = 12.56$ inches.

FIG. 63.—Graphical Means of constructing the Sinusoidal Projection.

The length of the central meridian is correct: $\pi R = 6.28$ inches.

Divide the Equator and the central meridian truly and similarly: if the meridians and the parallels are to be 15° apart, then the spaces on the two lines in question will be $2\pi R/24$ inches, though, of course, there will be twice as many spaces on the Equator as on the central meridian. The length of a parallel on the globe is $2\pi R \cos$ lat., and so 15° of longitude

112

n any parallel is found by dividing this amount by
4 (fig. 64).

Having worked this out for each parallel, we may draw

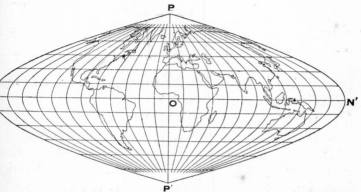

FIG. 64.—World Map on the Sinusoidal Projection.
[*c.* 1/428,000,000.]

e meridians as smooth curves, which are, in fact, sine
rves, through the corresponding points on each
rallel.[1]

The lettering on fig. 64 refers to the graphical construction; the
re itself is constructed trigonometrically, and hence the lettering
uld be used only for general guidance.

CHAPTER XII

THE CHOICE OF PROJECTIONS

IN choosing a projection for a map, there are two main points to consider :

1. What is the purpose of the map ?

2. What is the extent of the area to be represented ?

The projection should fulfil both these considerations. The matter will be made clearer by considering various examples. Let us suppose a map is required to show the distribution of the chief rice-producing areas of the world. An equal-area map will meet the case best because it enables the reader to obtain at a glance an idea of the respective sizes of each area. But a map of the whole world is necessary. The question then resolves itself into finding a suitable equal-area projection of the whole world. The chief rice areas are in tropical and sub-tropical regions, and so it does not matter very much if high northern and southern areas are distorted or even left out. At the same time it is always as well to have a projection which is easy to draw. The choice, therefore, seems to fall to the cylindrical equal-area. All the parallels and meridians are straight lines, the distortion of shape within 30° of the Equator is not too great (all the main rice areas are thus included), and although the east and west exaggeration of the polar areas is very great, this need not affect the actual purpose for which the map is required.

But such considerations would not hold for a map of the main wheat areas of the world. These are nearly all in temperate latitudes and in both hemispheres. The areas are also very large and, as far as possible, their shape should be maintained within fair reason. In this case a cylindrical projection is not so suitable because of the distortion in temperate latitudes. The choice, then, is between the sinusoidal, Mollweide, and Aitoff. The relative advantages and disadvantages of these having been considered, probably Mollweide[1] would be chosen, as it is easier to draw than Aitoff and gives a better representation of shape than the sinusoidal. In atlases other projections—usually some form of cylindrical—are used, but there does not seem to be very much to be said in their favour.[2] Should, however, an equal-area map of a country or continent be desired (as, for example, an administrative map of the United States, or one showing the distribution of maize in the United States), the considerations which have governed our choice so far can no longer apply. A conical or modified conical will be most suitable. There are at least four possible projections: the simple conic with two standard parallels, the conical equal-area with one standard parallel, Alber's conical equal-area, and Bonne's. Of these the first is not strictly equal-area, and if equivalence of areas is particularly desired will not be chosen. But if only a close approximation to equivalence is required, the simplicity of its construction may more than outweigh its disadvantages. Of the two conical

---

[1] Mollweide's and Aitoff's projections are discussed in Part II.

[2] In atlases, especially economic atlases, uniformity seems to be the ruling factor in distribution maps. Partly for this reason Gall's stereographic projection (q.v.) is much used.

equal-area projections, Alber's would be chosen because the scale is correct along two parallels instead of one, and because there is a more effective distribution of error than in the conical equal-area with one standard parallel. In that projection the parallels are arcs of circles and the meridians are straight lines. It is not used very much for atlas maps at present. Nevertheless, the actual construction, apart from the mathematical calculation, is easy. At the present time Bonne's projection would probably be used ; it is well known, and, for an area no larger than the United States or Europe, there is not much distortion. Further, the scale along all parallels is true, and as Europe and the United States have their greatest extent in this direction they are well suited to this projection. Asia, however, is not well represented on this projection ; it has too great an extent east and west and also north and south, so that towards the north-west and north-east corners the meridians and parallels are very oblique to one another. Thus there is great distortion in these regions. Hence for an equal-area map of Asia, Lambert's zenithal equal-area projection is more appropriate. It is more difficult to draw and to compute, however.

Smaller areas, such as the British Isles, France, etc., present very little difficulty. Their extent is so small that on ordinary atlas maps it is very hard to detect differences between similar projections. For this reason those graticules which are most easily drawn are generally chosen. The simple conic, with two standard parallels, is most suitable, but not very commonly used.

Zenithal projections naturally lend themselves to polar areas. In fact, we may say that, other things being equal, a cylindrical projection is suitable for equatorial regions, a conical for temperate regions, and a zenithal for polar regions. But for World maps—apart from Mercator and possibly the cylindrical equal-area—the cylindrical graticules are not well adapted. A conventional form is commonly employed—Mollweide or Aitoff. The former is sometimes developed [1] in two hemispheres. For maps including anything up to a hemisphere a zenithal projection, with the point of tangency on the Equator or at some point other than the Poles, is well suited.

There are many maps constructed for some special purpose to which all other considerations must give place. Mercator is the best-known case. Some of the polar maps come under this group. For exploration purposes a zenithal equidistant is suggested, since all meridional distances are correct, as are also all azimuths from the Pole. As the Polar Areas are all included in a circle of $23\frac{1}{2}°$ radius from the Pole, the error in areas is kept very small, and so there is but little point in having resort to the zenithal equal-area projection.

Because air-transport over land and sea is equally simple, it follows that great-circle routes may be more closely followed in this than in any other means of transport. Thus the gnomonic or great-circle projection has a peculiar value in this respect. The main disadvantage of gnomonic maps is that with increasing distance from the centre of the map there is a very rapid increase in the exaggeration of the scale. This is a great but not an insuperable objection. If a series of gnomonic projections be made, great-circle courses can be continued from one sheet to another, as in the case of the cubical development described on page 132. Such geometrical

[1] As an example of this, see Bartholomew's *Oxford Atlas*.

developments are infinite : the Earth can be developed on a solid of any number of sides, and each " side " is then a gnomonic projection for the area to which it corresponds. If, further, such a development of the World be made so that a large city or an important air base is at or near the centre of each side, so much the better, because, for obvious reasons, such places are likely to be the main foci of aeronautical and commercial activity in a given region.[1]

Quite another series of considerations must be made if a map were required to show a railway line such as the Cape to Cairo line. This railway extends practically equal distances north and south of the Equator ; its course is very nearly north and south, deviating but little from the meridian. A map to show equal distances in a north and south direction is suggested, and probably the zenithal equidistant projection would be chosen with the centre on the Equator at the point where the 33rd meridian east of Greenwich cuts it.[2]

Distance in an east-and-west direction is also easy to show. In all conical projections the scale is true at least along one parallel. Thus for a map to show the Trans-Siberian Railway and a small area on each side of it a simple conical would be suitable. The curvature of the parallel (in this case 55° N.) on a simple conical would not differ very much from the curvature of the same parallel on the conic with two standard parallels, and would be the same as that on Bonne. But the Trans-Siberian line deviates rather considerably from the 55th parallel ;

[1] The Royal Air Force have adopted Mercator's projection for air maps, for reasons similar to those governing its use in sea-navigation.

[2] The sinusoidal would do equally well, the central meridian being 33° E. long.

because of this it would perhaps be better to make use of the conic with two standard parallels. If, as in the case of the Canadian and United States boundary, a parallel of latitude is either taken as the frontier or adhered to very closely, then the simple conic can be used just as well.

The representation of population is an important matter. For very large regions, equivalence of area appears to be the main point at issue, so that one can compare easily the size of the areas concerned. For small areas on a large scale many other considerations occur, and the representation of population becomes a very difficult matter. In a map of the periphery of the Indian Ocean, India and North-Western Australia can be represented truly in area ; one can at once make an estimate of the distribution and density of their populations. But if the main winds and ocean currents of the same area were to be represented on such a map, an equal-area projection would be no longer suitable. Direction is the most important criterion, and Mercator's projection is best for this purpose.

Finally, a word may be added about maps showing a whole hemisphere. Nearly all atlases give such maps of the world, but there seems to be no special justification for them other than conventionality. The somewhat ineffective globular projection is still much used. If hemisphere maps are needed, it is probably better that they should possess some definite property. Mollweide can be adapted, as in Bartholomew's *Oxford Atlas*, and the zenithal equal-area and the zenithal equidistant are good. For World maps the representation in two hemispheres has this advantage—shapes are not so greatly distorted as in a complete Mollweide or Aitoff. On the other hand, the gap between the two hemispheres is awkward.

PART II

CHAPTER I

PART I. THE OBLIQUE CASE OF THE GNOMONIC PROJECTION

THE two cases of the gnomonic projection already described are comparatively simple. The oblique case not so, and is rather laborious. However, no great mathematical knowledge is required in understanding the method of construction; the difficulty lies in the great mass of calculations that have to be made before the graticule can be drawn.

The plane on which the projection is made may be tangent to the globe at any point other than the Poles and the Equator. A little thought will show that the meridians, being great circles, must again be straight lines and the parallels will be curves convex to the Equator.

In fig. 65 the plane DLV is tangent to the globe at C. Let α be the latitude of C.

It can be seen that LCV is the projection of the meridian L′CV′, and that V is the position of the Pole on the projection. L, on the other hand, is the projection of the point L′, which is on the Equator. The Equator, a great circle, must also be a straight line.

Again, DHV is the projection of the meridian D′H′V′. The difference in longitude between the meridians L′CV′ and D′H′V′ is χ, and this symbol is used throughout this chapter to denote longitude as measured from the central meridian L′CV′.

The first step in the construction is to draw a perpendicular from C to VD, meeting VD in H, which is point on any meridian, in this case on DHV.[1]

Then, since C is the tangent point and O the centre of projection, the plane HCO will be perpendicular t

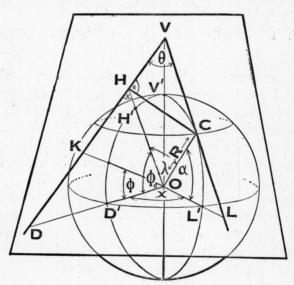

FIG. 65.—The Construction of the Oblique Case of the Gnomonic Projection.

the tangent plane along the line HC, and the line D will be perpendicular to this plane, HCO, since CH drawn perpendicular to DV. It therefore follows tha VH is perpendicular to HO in the plane VHO; that i the angle VHO is a right angle.

HCO is a right-angled triangle with the right ang at C, and tan λ = CH/R, where R = CO, the radiu of the globe.

[1] See also Plate III.

THE OBLIQUE CASE OF THE GNOMONIC

The triangle VOD is right-angled at O, and because H is perpendicular to DV, $OH^2 = VH \times HD$.

Let the angle $HOD = \phi_0$; then

$$\tan \phi_0 = \frac{DH}{OH} = \frac{OH}{HV} = \frac{DH}{R \sec \lambda} = \frac{DH \cos \lambda}{R}.$$

Again, let the angle $KOD = \phi$; then

$$(\phi_0 - \phi) = \frac{KH}{OH}, \text{ thus } KH = R \sec \lambda \tan (\phi_0 - \phi).$$

Now $HV = R \sec \lambda \cot \phi_0$

$$VK = R \sec \lambda [\tan (\phi_0 - \phi) + \cot \phi_0]$$

and $CH = CV \sin \theta = R \sin \theta \cot \alpha$.

(VHC is a triangle, right-angled at H; and θ is the angle subtended at V, the pole of the projection, by the longitude.)

But since $CH = R \sin \theta \cot \alpha$; $\tan \lambda = \sin \theta \cot \alpha$.

$$DH = \frac{OH^2}{VH} = \frac{R^2 \sec^2 \lambda}{CV \cos \theta} = \frac{R \tan \alpha}{\cos \theta \cos^2 \lambda}$$

and as the angles DLV and DLO are right angles, it follows that :

$$DL = LO \tan \chi = R \sec \alpha \tan \chi,$$

$$\text{and that } LV = \frac{R}{\sin \alpha \cos \alpha},$$

because $LV = LC + CV$

$$= R \tan \alpha + R \cot \alpha$$

$$= R \left(\frac{\sin \alpha}{\cos \alpha} + \frac{\cos \alpha}{\sin \alpha} \right)$$

$$= \frac{R}{\sin \alpha \cos \alpha}, \text{ since } \sin^2 \alpha + \cos^2 \alpha = 1.$$

Finally, $\tan \theta = \frac{LD}{LV}$

$$= \frac{R \sec \alpha \tan \chi \sin \alpha \cos \alpha}{R}$$

$$= \tan \chi \sin \alpha.$$

Having proceeded so far, the next step is to wo out for all the parallels and meridians necessary t points of intersection. The points have to be obtain by a rather roundabout process.

Assuming we require an oblique gnomonic projecti of North America on a plane tangent at the poi where the 100th meridian of west longitude crosses t 45th parallel of north latitude, and the scale of t map is to be 1/50,000,000, the following equatio must be worked out in full for as many points as a wanted.

(1) To find the distance apart of the meridians the Equator. (In this particular case it is not actual wanted, but is added for clearness.)

$$DL = R \sec \alpha \tan \chi.$$

Example (in the examples four-figure tables have be used and also logarithms to shorten the calculations).- Distance of $10°$ (W. or E. of the central meridian).

$$\log DL = 0\cdot6990 + 0\cdot1505 + \bar{1}\cdot2463 = 0\cdot0958,$$
$$\text{and antilog} = 1\cdot2470 \text{ inches.}$$

(2) To find θ. $\operatorname{Tan} \theta = \tan \chi \sin \alpha$.

Example.—

$\chi = 10°$, $\log \tan \theta = 1\cdot2463 + \bar{1}\cdot8495 = \bar{1}\cdot0958$, an $\theta = 7° 6'$.

(3) To find CH. $CH = R \sin \theta \cot \alpha$.

*Example.—*CH for $10°$ of longitude west or east the central meridian.

$$\log CH = 0\cdot6990 + \bar{1}\cdot0920 + 0\cdot0000 = \bar{1}\cdot7910$$
$$\text{and antilog.} = 0\cdot6180 \text{ inches.}$$

(4) To find λ. $\operatorname{Tan} \lambda = \sin \theta \cot \alpha$.

Example.—

χ (long.) $= 10°$; $\log \tan \lambda = \bar{1}\cdot0920 + 0\cdot0000$, an $\lambda = 7° 3'$.

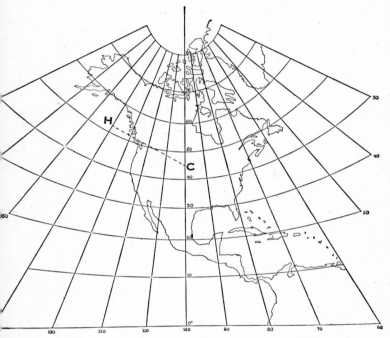

PLATE III.—OBLIQUE GNOMONIC PROJECTION OF NORTH AMERICA.

[*c.* 1/142,000,000.]

127

(5) To find DH. $DH = \dfrac{R \tan a}{\cos \theta \cos^2 \lambda}$.

Example.—When $\chi = 10°$, $\theta = 7° 6'$, and $\lambda = 7° 3'$.

$$\begin{aligned}
\log. DH &= 0\cdot6990 + 0\cdot0000 - (\bar{1}\cdot9967 + \bar{1}\cdot9934) \\
&= 0\cdot6990 - \bar{1}\cdot9901 = 0\cdot7089
\end{aligned}$$

and antilog $= 5\cdot1160$ inches.

(6) To find $\tan \phi_0$. $\tan \phi_0 = \dfrac{\cos \lambda \; DH}{R}$.

Example.—

When $\chi = 10°$, $\lambda = 7° 3'$, and $DH = 5\cdot1160$ inches.

$$\begin{aligned}
\log \tan \phi_0 &= \bar{1}\cdot9968 + 0\cdot7089 - 0\cdot6990 \\
&= 0\cdot7057 - 0\cdot6990 = 0\cdot0067
\end{aligned}$$

and $\phi_0 = 45° 26'$.

(7) To find KH. $KH = R \sec \lambda \tan (\phi_0 - \phi)$.

Example.—When $\chi = 10°$, $\lambda = 7° 3'$, $\phi_0 - \phi = 0° 26$ (i.e. lat. 45° N.).

$$\log KH = 0\cdot6990 + 0\cdot0032 + \bar{3}\cdot8787 = \bar{2}\cdot5809,$$

and antilog $= 0\cdot03810$ inches, and so on for all values of χ

To plot the projection draw a straight line as the central meridian, and take any point on it such as C. Then rule off lengths equal to CV and CL respectively (i.e. the cotangent and tangent of latitude of C) (see fig. 65 and Plate III).

The perpendiculars, CH, may then be put in for as many meridians as necessary. Since CHV is a right-angled triangle, the angles at C are equal to 90° — θ (see 2 above). Having obtained the point H, join VH and produce it as far as required. Then KH for all parallels should be found and marked off from H along VH produced, working outwards from H. This same process holds good for all meridians, the next succeeding meridian being found when CH is constructed for—say—20° and so on. All points must be plotted separately;

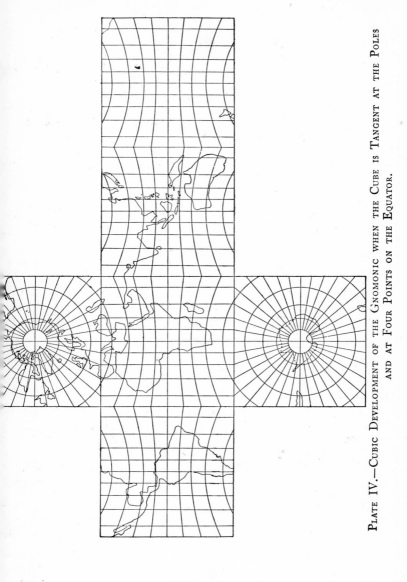

PLATE IV.—CUBIC DEVELOPMENT OF THE GNOMONIC WHEN THE CUBE IS TANGENT AT THE POLES AND AT FOUR POINTS ON THE EQUATOR.

though, as the projection is symmetrical about its centra
meridian, a little trouble can be saved by marking o
points at once on meridians east and west of the centra
meridian and equidistant from it.

The oblique case possesses the same merits as do th
polar and equatorial cases (q.v.).

PART 2. THE CUBIC DEVELOPMENT OF THE GNOMONI
PROJECTION

We have now obtained a gnomonic projection for an
plane—whether tangent at the Poles, the Equator, or a
some point between the Poles and the Equator. We ar
thus able to undertake the construction of a gnomoni
projection on a circumscribed cube. Imagine a hollo
cube placed round the globe so that the poles touch th
mid-points of two opposite sides of the cube. Th
remaining four sides will be tangent planes to th
Equator at points 90° apart. It is clear that any poir
on the Equator may be made the centre of one of th
equatorial planes. In order to construct the whol
map two ordinary polar gnomonic charts and fou
equatorial charts are necessary. Clearly each equatori
chart will show 90° of latitude and 90° of longitude–
i.e. 45° of latitude or longitude on each side of th
mid-point. Each polar face will show 360° of longitud
and 45° of latitude (see Plate IV).

But it may be desired to have a place such as Londo
at, or near, the centre of one face. If London wer
adopted, we must then imagine the hollow cube s
placed that the mid-point of one face is in latitud
50° N., longitude 0°. The mid-point of the opposit
face will then be in latitude 50° S. and longitude 180° E
or W. The remaining four faces will be displace

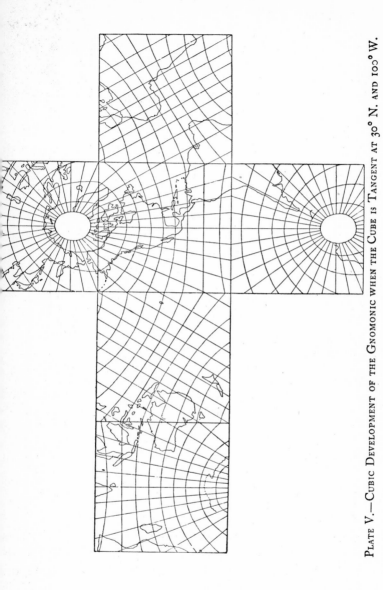

PLATE V.—CUBIC DEVELOPMENT OF THE GNOMONIC WHEN THE CUBE IS TANGENT AT 30° N. AND 100° W.

similarly. This arrangement will obviously be of great
value than the simpler polar and equatorial case, becau
it is clearly an advantage to have a big town or city
the centre of a face. Such a place might well be t
headquarters of a national air force or of an air rou
organisation (see Plate V).

There are other possible geometrical projections
this type ; world maps may be developed on octahedr
dodecahedra, and icosahedra. The construction

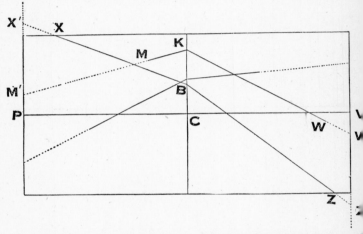

Fig. 66.—Great-circle Courses on the Cubic Development of tl
Gnomonic.

similar in each case, but it is doubtful if there is al
real advantage obtained in multiplying the number
faces of the figure on which the projection is to
made.

PART 3. THE CONSTRUCTION OF GREAT-CIRCLE COURS
ON THE CUBIC DEVELOPMENT OF THE GNOMONIC

It has been shown that a great-circle course on
gnomonic projection is a straight line. Thus it is

ery simple matter to insert a great-circle course between ny two points on one face of the cube. But the problem ith which we are concerned is to continue such a great ircle on to the next face.

In fig. 66 suppose XB to be the great-circle course on ne face of the cube. In order to find its continuation n the next face, we must find the position of Z'. PCV a line joining the mid-points of the three parallel dges. By symmetry, Z' must be as much below PV s X' is above it. It will be noticed that there is no eed to assume that the edges of the cube faces are mited; they may be produced as far as necessary.

If a great-circle course is required between any two oints such as M and W on two adjacent faces, a point, ., must first be found on the common edge in such a osition that the intercepts PM' and VW' are equal. 'his point K is found by trial.

CHAPTER II

PART 1. THE OBLIQUE STEREOGRAPHIC PROJECTION

A STEREOGRAPHIC projection can be made on any other plane than the two already described. The principle of construction are just the same as in these cases, so that a brief description is all that is necessary.

In fig. 67 let S′B be the plane on which the projection is to be made.

P is " the source of light." M, the point of tangency of the plane and the globe, is in 30° N. lat.

O is the centre of the globe, and EQ is the Equator.

Draw meridians for every degree required—15° in the figure—and then draw lines such as PQ, PN, PF, PS, and so on, producing them to meet the plane.

Clearly the North Pole in this case is 60° N. of M, and therefore, its distance from M on the plane is 2R tan 30° (see page 41), or, geometrically, the distance MN′.

Similarly, the distance on the plane of any other point from M = 2R tan $\frac{1}{2}d$, where d is the difference in degrees of the latitude of M and the point in question.

For example : the parallel of 60° S. is 90° from M and therefore at a distance of 2R tan 45°, or, geometrically, M, V.

Thus to construct the parallels, first draw a circle to represent the sphere (fig. 68) on the required scale and then draw in the vertical axis. The centre of the sphere is, in this case, 30° N. lat., and the Pole is found

by setting off from O, the centre, a distance equal to 2R
an 30.

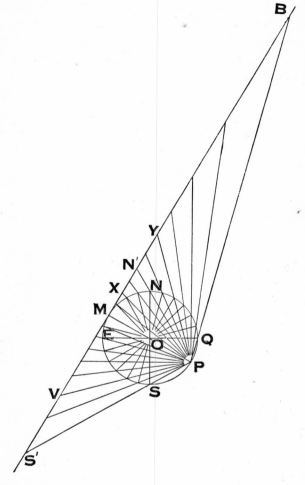

FIG. 67.—Construction of the Oblique Case of the Stereographic.

The other parallels are marked similarly on the vertical
xis, which is also the central meridian.

135

The next problem is to find the centres of these circles. Geometrically their radii can be taken from such a diagram as fig. 67. For example, if the centre of 60° N. lat. is required, we must consider the two intersections of this parallel on the plane, i.e. at X and Y. Clearly the required radius must be $\frac{1}{2}$XY. But it is inconvenient to have to refer to a second diagram, and it is not difficult to obtain the radii directly. The distance of the first intersection of any parallel from the centre of the map is—as given above—2R tan $\frac{1}{2}d$. The distance from the centre of the second intersection is 2R tan $\frac{1}{2}$ (angular distance of centre of map from Pole + the angular distance of the parallel in question from the Pole). For example, 45° N. :

First intersection . . 2R tan $\frac{1}{2}$ 15°
Second „ . . 2R tan $\frac{1}{2}$ (60° + 45°)

The centre of the circle required is then at half the distance between the two intersections, and can be found directly by measuring off this distance, along the central meridian produced, from the first intersection.

The other parallels are added in a similar way. It is important to note that the parallel which is as many degrees south of the Equator as the parallel on which the plane is tangent is north of the Equator, or vice versa, is a straight line, because it passes through the point of sight—30° S. in fig. 67.

Parallels still farther south will have their centres on the prolongation of the axis. Those parallels south of the straight parallel—i.e. the one through P—are struck from centres on the central meridian, and their curvature will be opposed to that of the parallels on the opposite side of the straight parallel.

THE OBLIQUE STEREOGRAPHIC

The meridians must pass through the Poles, and their
entres will lie on a line which cuts the vertical axis at
 point midway between the Poles. It is thus necessary
 find, first of all, the position of the South Pole. In
he case under consideration the South Pole is 120° S.
f the centre of the map. That is to say, the Pole is
n the central meridian at a distance of 2R tan 60°

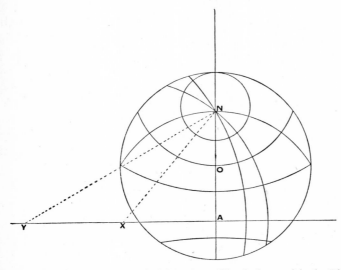

IG. 68.—Oblique Stereographic Map of one Hemisphere with the **Plane**
of Projection Tangent at 30° N. on the Greenwich Meridian.

om O. Having found this point, a horizontal line can
e drawn half-way between the two Poles. The centres
f the meridians are all on this line.

It was shown in the equatorial case that the centres
f the meridians were distant from the intersection of
he central meridian and the Equator as R times the
otangent of the longitude.[1] A similar relation holds
ere, but instead of R cot long. we must substitute

[1] See footnote, p. 44.

NA cot long.—i.e. NA is the radius of the meridian passing through both Poles.

(In fig. 68 XA = NA cot 50° and YA = NA cot 30°) The radii (XN and YN) for constructing the meridian

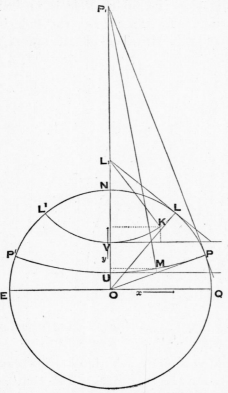

are respectively NA cosec 50° and NA cosec 30°.

PART 2. A SIMPLE MEANS OF CONSTRUCTING LARGE-SCALE STEREOGRAPHIC MAPS (cf. Ch. IX, pt. 1

For purposes of transformation which are described later, and for making large-scale wall maps, the stereographic projection does not lend itself to direct construction on account of the very great radii required to draw the parallels and the meridians. The following method may be employed

FIG. 69.—Construction of the Parallels on Large-scale Stereographic Maps.

in the equatorial case, though it is rather tedious. However, it involves but an elementary knowledge of mathematics, and is described here for that reason.

Let L and P be two points on latitudes 50° N. and 20° N. respectively (fig. 69).

Then $L_1L = R \cot 50°$ and
$$P_1P = R \cot 20°.$$

Also the angles at L_1 and P_1 are 50° and 20° respectively. The points L, V, and L', and P, U, and P' on these two parallels are known already. But other points are required on these parallels. Since the spacing of the meridians is not regular, it is not easy to obtain the points of the actual intersections. However, by dividing the angles LL_1O and PP_1O into a given number of equal parts, points such as K and M may be found by ordinary co-ordinates.

The position of K is found thus : Suppose the angle $KL_1O = 36°$, or ·72 of the angle LL_1O. Then, because $L_1K = r$, $x = r \sin 36°$ and $y = r - r \cos 36°$, when V is origin (as in the rectangular co-ordinates for simple conic). In this way a series of points on lat. 50° can be found, and then it may be drawn in as a smooth curve. In the same way M is found. Suppose the angle $MP_1O = 10°$, or $\frac{1}{2}$ angle PP_1O. Then $x = r \sin 10°$, and $y = r - r \cos 10°$, where U is taken as origin.

The meridians may be plotted in the same way. Suppose M and L (fig. 70) are the intersections of any two meridians, X_1 and X_2, with the Equator. The radii required to draw these meridians are FS and QS—— R times the cosecants of the longitudes [1]; the distances from the centre O, OF, and OQ are R times the cotangents of the longitudes of M and L respectively.[1]

The angle $SQO = X_1$ and the angle $SFO = X_2$. A point such as H may be plotted if the value of the angle HQO is known. As before, divide the angle SQO into a given number of equal parts, and suppose the

[1] See footnote, p. 44.

angle HQO = 20°. Then the co-ordinates giving the position of H are :

$$x = r - r \cos 20°$$

$$y = r \sin 20°, \text{ where } r = R \text{ cosec longitude, and}$$

L is taken as origin.

In this way all the meridians may be completed.

PART 3. THE ORTHOMORPHISM OF THE STEREOGRAPHIC

That the stereographic is an orthomorphic projection

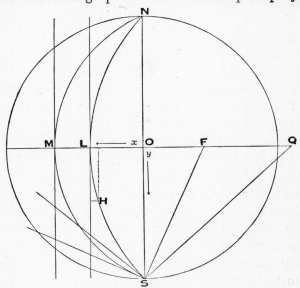

FIG. 70.—Construction of the Meridians on Large-scale Stereographic Maps.

in the strict sense of the word may be shown quite readily. There is no need to show that the meridians and the parallels are at right angles, for this is apparent from the construction.

That the scale is the same along parallel and meridian at any point of intersection can be shown best by the calculus, but it can also be shown by geometry or by trigonometry. We will, however, illustrate the property by a numerical example in the polar case. As an example, let us consider a small area at the intersection of the 40th parallel and any meridian. Suppose we take an area measuring 1° in latitude and in longitude. The radius (for the sake of clarity, R, the radius, is taken as 2″ as in previous examples) of lat. 40° on the projection is 2R tan 25° or 1″·865231. The scale along any one parallel is constant ; on the other hand, the scale along the meridians increases outwards, and is thus never the same at any two points. The radius required to draw latitude 49° 30′ is 2R tan 24° 45′ or 1″·844025 ; and the radius for latitude 50° 30′ is 2R tan 25° 15′ or 1″·886523. That is to say, the length of 1° of latitude bisected by the 40th parallel is 1″·886523 − 1″·8844025 = 0″·042498. But 1° along the parallel is equal to $2\pi r/360$ (where r = 1″·8652) or 0″·0325544. Thus there is a distinct discrepancy between an arc of 1° along the parallel and the meridian. Suppose a smaller area is considered—an area measuring 4′ of arc along meridian and parallel. Because the longitude scale along any parallel is constant, 4′ of arc (1/15th of a degree) = 0·03255/15 = 0″·0021702 9.[1] The interval of latitude between 49° 58′ and 50° 2′ is again equal to the difference between their respective radii—or 1″·8666472 − 1″·8638144 = 0″·0028328.[1] Thus the scales along meridian and parallel are becoming closer, and if the same process were repeated for still smaller arcs, they would be seen to get closer and closer together until finally, when the ultimate stage is reached—a point—they would coincide. In this sense the stereographic is orthomorphic.

[1] The calculations were worked with seven-figure tables. Four-figure tables are not sufficiently accurate.

CHAPTER III

PART 1. LA HIRE'S PROJECTION

THIS projection is seldom used, and is described here as a type of zenithal projection of the perspective group in which the source of light is exterior to the sphere and is situated at a point somewhere between the stereographic and the orthographic positions.

La Hire takes a point situated at $1 + \dfrac{1}{\sqrt{2}}$, or 1·71 times the radius of the Earth from the centre (fig. 71). If from

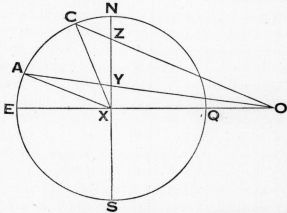

FIG. 71.—Diagram illustrating the Construction of La Hire's Projection

such a point rays be drawn to two points on the meridian SEACN and distant $22\frac{1}{2}°$ and $67\frac{1}{2}°$ from N., the distances XY and XZ are—to two places of decimals—0·25 and 0·75 times XN respectively. Thus if the map be projected

n the plane NS, a satisfactory map is produced. **To**
1ake a polar map, draw lines from O for every 10°
or whatever interval is desired) and note where they
ut the line NS. Then with radii XY, XZ, and so on,
escribe concentric circles, as in the case of the other
enithal projections. The meridians are put in in the
sual way. The resulting map will be almost indistin-
uishable from a zenithal equidistant. The projection
; difficult to construct if one of the Poles is not taken
s centre of the map.

PART 2. VAN DER GRINTEN'S PROJECTION

This is a projection of the whole sphere which is
ometimes found in atlases. The complete sphere is
ontained within one circle. It has no particular
roperties and is of little practical importance. How-
ver, it gives a fair representation of the World, having
either the great east and west extension of the Mercator
n high latitudes, nor the compression in similar latitudes
vhich is a defect of the sinusoidal and the Mollweide
rojections.

The diagram (fig. 72) will make the construction
lear.

Draw, to scale, a circle to represent the globe (fig. 72).
/Q is the Equator and NS the central meridian. Join
NV. Divide NO into a given number of equal parts
—in this case 6. Then draw lines EE', DD', from
hese points and parallel to VQ. Join EQ and DQ,
:tc., noting where these lines cut the central meridian.
Next join LQ, KQ, etc., and, from the points where
hese lines cut the central meridian, construct the dotted
barallel lines, such as CC'. The parallels of latitude are

then constructed by passing circles through poin
bearing the same degree number—e.g. 60° and 60°.

Similar divisions can be marked off along the arc NQ.

The Equator is then divided equally, and the meridia
are drawn as circles passing through the Poles and th
corresponding points on the Equator.

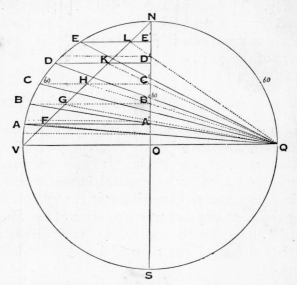

FIG. 72.—Diagram illustrating the Construction of Van der Grinten'
Projection.

PART 3. GALL'S STEREOGRAPHIC PROJECTION

This is a projection of the cylindrical type, but th
cylinder is supposed to cut the globe so that the par
between parallels 45° N. and S. is outside the cylinder
The projection is then constructed stereographically
It is sometimes used for World maps to show distributions. Many of the maps in Bartholomew's *Atlas o
Economic Geography* (L. W. Lyde) are on this projection

The spacing of the parallels is similar to the stereographic, but instead of using the formula $2R \tan \frac{1}{2}\phi$, substitute $1 \cdot 7071 R \tan \frac{1}{2}\phi$.[1] The graphical construction just as easy. The meridians are spaced correctly along parallels 45° N. and S.—i.e. $2\pi R d \cos 45°$, where d is the interval of longitude expressed as a fraction of the

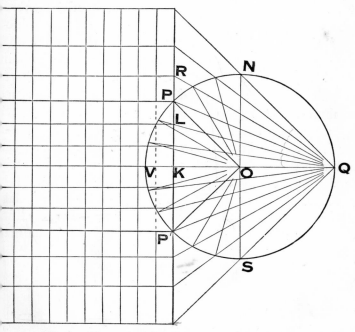

Fig. 73.—Diagram illustrating the Construction of Gall's Stereographic Projection.

circumference of 45° latitude N. or S. The scale is true along these two parallels only; on the equatorial

In the triangle POK, PO = R, and the angle POK = 45°. Thus KO = R cos 45° or $0 \cdot 7071R$, and therefore KL, KP, KR, etc. $(R + 0 \cdot 7071R) \tan \frac{1}{2}\phi = 1 \cdot 7071 \tan \frac{1}{2}\phi$, where ϕ is the latitude and is unity.

sides of the forty-fives it is too small ; on the polar side it is too great. The meridian scale is everywhere to great except between the standard parallels, where it too small. It is neither equal-area nor orthomorphic, bu serves to make a fair map of the World (fig. 73).

The method described above appears to be that use in some atlases. Strictly speaking, the adjective " Stered graphic " is not applicable to it, if by stereographic meant projection from a fixed point on the sphere on a plane perpendicular to the diameter through the poin However, it would be just as easy to use the normal stered graphic method ; the parallels, instead of being space at intervals of $1\cdot7071$ R tan $\frac{1}{2}\phi$ would then be space by means of the formula 2R tan $\frac{1}{2}\phi$. The meridi; spacing would be the same in both cases. The on difference would be that the parallels would be rath farther apart in the true stereographic case. It doubtful if the utility of the map would be appreciab affected. It will be obvious that many other modific tions could be made—e.g. other parallels could be ma true instead of 45° N. and S.

CHAPTER IV

PART 1. LA CARTE PARALLÉLOGRAMMATIQUE, OR DIE RECHTECKIGE PLATTKARTE

THIS is an unimportant and very conventional cylindrical projection with no particular English name. Two parallels at equal distances from the Equator are chosen as " standard parallels " and are divided correctly.

As an example, let us compute the required figures for a map of the World, in which 30° N. and S. are taken as the standards. The length of an arc of 10° of longitude along these parallels is $\dfrac{2\pi R \cos 30°}{36}$ or $0''\cdot1511$, if the scale be 1/250,000,000. The parallels are spaced at equal intervals apart along the meridians : $\dfrac{\pi R}{18} = 0''\cdot174$. In this way a series of rectangles is constructed, hence the name.

It corresponds to the simple conic with two standard parallels. It has no particular merit and is not used in atlases. It appears to have been used to some extent instead of Mercator in the time of the great discoveries, and as late as the beginning of the nineteenth century (Groll-Graf.)

PART 2. THE CYLINDRICAL EQUAL-AREA WITH TWO STANDARD PARALLELS

As in the " carte parallélogrammatique," two parallels are chosen as standards and are divided truly. The area, however, between any parallel and the Equator is to remain equal to the corresponding area on the globe, i.e. $2\pi Rh$ ($h = R \sin$ lat.). But the length of a standard parallel is $2\pi R \cos \phi$. If, therefore, the area of the zone be divided by the length of a standard parallel then the quotient is the distance of the parallel in question from the Equator. Calling this distance d, we have

$$d = \frac{2\pi Rh}{2\pi R \cos \phi} = \frac{h}{\cos \phi}.$$

The standard parallels are then divided correctly— $\frac{2\pi R \cos \phi}{360}$, and the graticule is constructed by drawing straight lines through these points to represent the meridians, and by drawing the remaining parallels in accordance with the above formula. Suppose 60° N and S. are taken as standards; they are distant from the Equator:

$$\frac{h}{\cos \phi} = \frac{R \sin 60°}{\cos 60°} = \frac{1 \times 0\cdot8660}{0\cdot5000} = 1''\cdot7320.$$

Similarly

latitude 40° is distant from the Equator 1·285 inches

,, 80° ,, ,, ,, 1·970 ,,

,, 90° ,, ,, ,, 2·000 ,,

The projection is comparatively unimportant and is very seldom used. It is the cylindrical case corresponding to Albers' conical equal-area with two standard parallels. It is also known as Behrmann's projection.

CHAPTER V

MOLLWEIDE'S PROJECTION

THIS is an equal-area projection of the whole sphere, and is an ellipse, whence its other name, the Elliptical Projection. It is a popular projection and occurs in most atlases for World maps showing distributions. It can be developed in hemispheres (see Bartholomew's *Oxford Atlas*) and can also be " interrupted " effectively p. 156).

The distortion towards the Poles is not as great as in the sinusoidal projection. The parallels are parallel straight lines, but are not equally spaced along the central meridian. The meridians are all ellipses, the central meridian being the special case in which the ellipse becomes a straight line, and the 90th meridian (reckoning from the centre of the map) being the other special case in which the ellipse becomes a circle.

The main problem is to obtain the correct spacing of the parallels along the central meridian.

The first step is to construct a circle equal in area to a hemisphere on the required scale. The area of a circle is πr^2, that of a hemisphere is $2\pi R^2$, and by equating these two expressions we have $\pi r^2 = 2\pi R^2$, whence $r = \sqrt{2}R$. Hence on a scale of 1/250,000,000, $R = 1$ and $r = 1\cdot414$. Describe a circle with this radius. Then produce the equatorial diameter each way, making

HF = HO, and KG = OK. Then describe the ellips‹
FANBGS (fig. 74).

Let DE be any parallel of latitude on the projection‹
and let /EOK be θ.

The area between any parallel of latitude on th‹
globe and the Equator is $2\pi R^2 \sin \phi$ ($\phi = $ lat.).

By construction, however, $2\pi R^2 \sin \phi$ is to be mad‹
equal to the area FABG.

But FABG is, by the properties of an ellipse, equal t‹

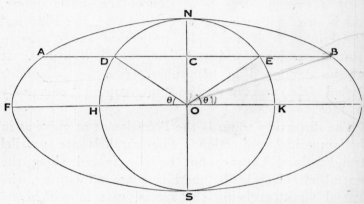

Fig. 74.—Construction of Mollweide's Projection.

twice the area HDEK ; and this again is equal to twi‹
△ OCE plus twice sector OKE.

The area of a sector is $\frac{1}{2}r^2 \theta$ (page 13) (θ in circula‹
measure).

The area of a triangle is $\frac{1}{2}r \sin \theta\, r \cos \theta = \frac{1}{4}r^2 \sin 2\,\theta$‹

Therefore, $\pi R^2 \sin \phi = 2\left(\frac{1}{2}r^2 \theta\right) + 2\left(\frac{1}{4}r^2 \sin 2\,\theta\right)$

$$= r^2\, \theta + \tfrac{1}{2}r^2 \sin 2\, \theta.$$

But $\qquad r = \sqrt{2}R.$

$\therefore \pi R^2 \sin \phi \quad = 2R^2\, \theta + R^2 \sin 2\theta$

and $\pi \sin \phi \quad = 2\, \theta + \sin 2\, \theta.$

Now, if θ is given, ϕ can be found.

Example.—Let $\theta = 40° = 0·6981$ radians.

$$2\theta = 1.3962 \text{ radians.}$$
$$\text{Sin } 2\theta = 0·9848.$$
$$\therefore \pi \sin \phi = 2·3810.$$
$$\therefore \log (\pi \sin \phi) = 0·3768.$$
$$\therefore \log \sin \phi = 0·3768 - \log \pi.$$
$$= 0·3768 - 0·4971.$$
$$= \overline{1}·8797.$$
$$\therefore \phi = 49° \ 18'.$$

By giving θ some values between 0° and 90°, a graph can be drawn from which the values of θ can be taken corresponding to any value of the latitude ϕ (fig. 75).

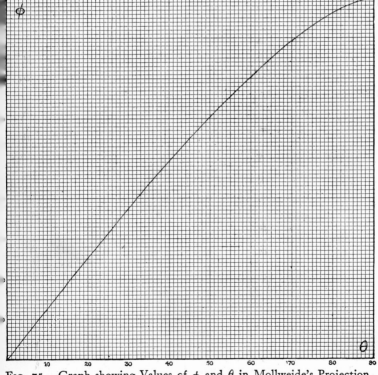

Fig. 75.—Graph showing Values of ϕ and θ in Mollweide's Projection.

In this way the following table can be constructed :

When $\theta = 10°$	$\phi = 12° 43'$,	or when $\phi = 10°$	$\theta = 8°$	o
$= 20°$	$= 25° 16'$	$= 20°$	$= 15°$	45
$= 30°$	$= 37° 31'$	$= 30°$	$= 24°$	o
$= 40°$	$= 49° 18'$	$= 40°$	$= 32°$	o
$= 50°$	$= 60° 22'$	$= 50°$	$= 40°$	30
$= 60°$	$= 70° 30'$	$= 60°$	$= 49°$	25
$= 70°$	$= 79° 18'$	$= 70°$	$= 59°$	30
$= 80°$	$= 86° 18'$	$= 80°$	$= 71°$	o
$= 90°$	$= 90° 0'$	$= 90°$	$= 90°$	o

N.B.—The latter table is taken from the graph o⟨r⟩ fig. 75, and so the values are only approximate.

Now, if $R = 1, r = 1·414$; then $1·414 : 1 :: 1 : 0·707$

Let OC, the distance between lat. DE and the Equato⟨r⟩ $= x$.

Then $x = r \sin \theta$.

Therefore x for $\phi = 10°$ is $1·414R \sin 8° = 1·414 \times 0·1392R = 0·1968R$, or in terms of r, $= 0·1968 \times 0·707r = 0·1391r$.[1]

In this way the following table is obtained* :

When $\phi = 10°$, then $x =$	$0·197R$	or $0·139r$
$20°$,	$0·384R$	$0·271r$
$30°$,	$0·575R$	$0·407r$
$40°$,	$0·749R$	$0·530r$
$50°$,	$0·921R$	$0·652r$
$60°$,	$1·074R$	$0·759r$
$70°$,	$1·218R$	$0·862r$
$80°$,	$1·337R$	$0·945r$
$90°$,	$1·414R$	$1·000r$

[1] $x = r \sin \theta$ . . . . (1)

$\quad = R\sqrt{2} \sin \theta$

$\quad = 1·414R \sin \theta$ . . . . (2)

* The values for R and r in above tables vary slightly from those give⟨n⟩ in other works since they have been calculated from approximate value⟨s⟩ of θ taken from the graph.

The data required for drawing the graticule are now ound. The parallels are put in with the help of the able. The meridians are then drawn. To do this, ach parallel must be divided into the required number f equal parts.

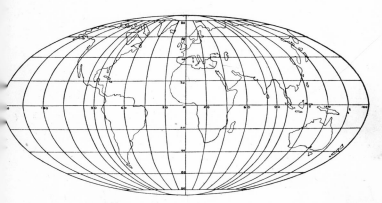

FIG. 76.—The World on Mollweide's Projection.

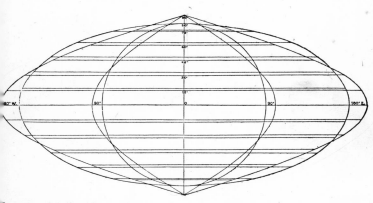

FIG. 77.—Mollweide and Sanson-Flamsteed Projections, to show Relations etween Parallels and the 90th and 180th Meridians East and West of the Central Meridian.

By construction, the length of the Equator

$$4r = 4 \times 1\cdot414R.$$

If, then, the meridians are to be 20° apart, they wi be at intervals of :

$$\frac{4 \times 1\cdot414}{18} = 0''\cdot314.$$

The length of any other parallel on the projection $4r \cos \theta$. Thus intervals of 20° of longitude on latitud 40° are found thus : Lat. (ϕ) 40° corresponds to (θ) 32°

Then $4r \cos 32° = 4 \times 1\cdot414 \times 0\cdot8480 = 4\cdot7963$, an

thus 20° of longitude $= \dfrac{4\cdot7960}{18} = 0\cdot2665$, if we take R=

The meridians are then drawn by passing curve through corresponding points on each parallel : the are all ellipses.

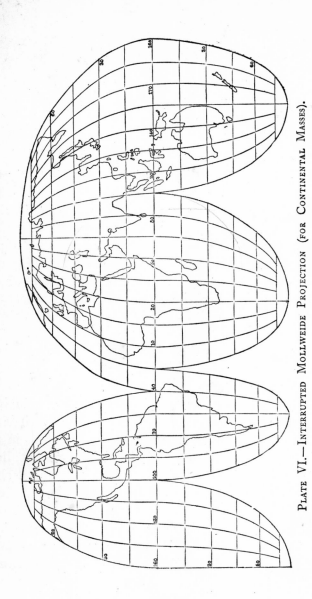

PLATE VI.—INTERRUPTED MOLLWEIDE PROJECTION (FOR CONTINENTAL MASSES).

CHAPTER VI

"INTERRUPTED" PROJECTIONS

An interesting development of Mollweide's projectic
is that known as the "Interrupted Mollweide." TI
projection is still equal-area, and the advantage gaine
by interrupting is that the breaks can be made in thos
parts which matter least. Plate VI shows such a pr
jection suited to the continents, the breaks coming ove
the oceans. It will be seen that the distortion towar
the Poles between the "interruptions" is not as great
in the normal case, and this fact, to some extent, mitigate
its awkward shape.

The sinusoidal may be constructed similarly, thoug
the shape is rather less pleasing than that of Mollweid
(Plate VII).

The principles of construction are the same in bot
cases. Certain meridians are chosen along which inter
ruptions are to be made, and others are chosen—in th
case in the land masses—and drawn as straight line
The spacing of the parallels is marked off along each o
these straight meridians and the parallels are sketched i
lightly. Each parallel is then divided as in the norm
cases, but here the divisions are marked outwards from
the straight meridians. All the required points havin
been obtained thus, the other meridians are drawn i
as smooth curves.

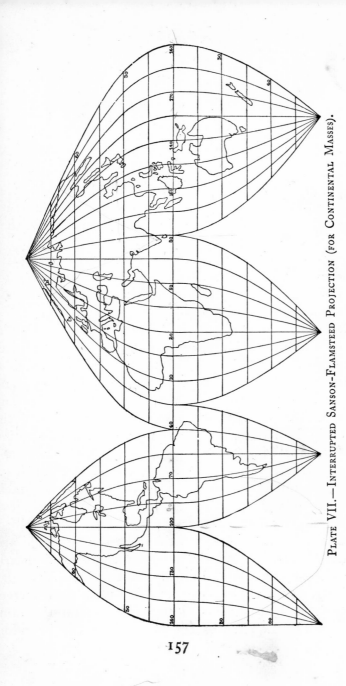

PLATE VII.—INTERRUPTED SANSON-FLAMSTEED PROJECTION (FOR CONTINENTAL MASSES).

157

CHAPTER VII

CONSTRUCTION OF MORE DIFFICULT CASES BY MEAN OF TRANSFORMATION

MANY projections in common use in atlases are not a all easy to make directly, and because the direct construc tion involves considerable mathematical knowledge, the will not be treated here in such a manner.

However, they can be constructed with comparativ ease by transformations. This method is in some case rather clumsy, but is helpful in that it avoids the us of mathematical calculations.

The main principle of transformation is quite simpl It consists in obtaining a medium whereby one projec tion can be " transformed " into another. In the pola cases of all the zenithal projections, the meridians an parallels form a series of radiating straight lines an concentric circles. The spacing of the meridians is tl same in each case ; the spacing of the parallels varie As far as drawing is concerned, they are all equally eas to construct. The equatorial and oblique cases, how ever, are not easy—except in one or two cases, notabl the stereographic and orthographic. The gnomonic fairly simple, but its shortcomings, already describe render it of much less use than the stereographic an orthographic. Thus the medium employed is near. always one of these, and usually the stereographic.

Let us take a general case. We have a polar stere graphic and an equatorial stereographic on the sam scale. The Equator of the former and the boundin meridian of the latter are circles of equal radius, and if we place them one upon the other, the polar case being drawn on tracing paper, these circles will coincide—as also the vertical and horizontal meridians of the polar case will with the central meridian and the Equator of the equatorial case. Clearly, then, any point on the polar case is in the same position relative to the Pole and to its vertical and horizontal meridians as the coincident point will be to the centre of the equatorial projection and the central meridian and Equator.

Suppose now we make a polar zenithal equidistant projection. This is similar to the polar stereographic, except that the spacing of the circles is different. How, then, can we make an equatorial equidistant ? We have seen that any point on the polar and equatorial stereographics can be defined with reference to two axes. But these two axes also exist in the case of the polar equidistant projection, and we can, therefore, refer any point already known on the two stereographic cases to the polar equidistant in the following way. A certain point can be taken on the equatorial stereographic, and when the tracing of the polar stereographic is placed over it, the point will be found to lie in a certain position within one of the quadrilaterals or meshes formed by the meridians and parallels of the polar case. It is easy, then, to place this point in the same *relative* position in the corresponding quadrilateral or mesh of the polar equidistant. Similarly, any other point can be so " transformed."

If, however, the points taken are the intersections of the meridians and parallels in the equatorial stereographic, the same points, when placed on the polar equidistant, will obviously represent the intersections of

the meridians and parallels of the equatorial equidistan
and by joining up corresponding points by smooth curv
we have an equatorial equidistant obtained by means c
transformation.

Consider first a simple case. A zenithal equal-are
projection of the World in hemispheres is require
First of all construct an equatorial stereographic on th
required scale. (The reason for this is explained later
Then, on tracing paper, make a polar stereographi
extending outwards so as to include the Equator. The
place the latter over the former, "setting" them s
that the bounding meridian of the equatorial cas
coincides with the Equator of the other, and the Equato
and the central meridian of the equatorial case coincid
with any two meridians of the polar case. The nex
step is to mark with a point on the tracing paper eac
intersection of the meridians and parallels on the equa
torial case. It is clear that the points so obtained bear
direct relation to the meridians and parallels of the pola
graticule, and any such point can be readily defined.

A polar equal-area graticule is next made on th
same scale as the stereographic graticule. Reference t
the cases already described on pages 57 and 41 will sho
that the distances between the parallels in the latter cas
increase away from the Pole, whereas in the forme
case they decrease—in other words, the two sets c
circles are not coincident. But the points obtained o
the tracing paper can easily be placed in their sam
relative positions on the equal-area graticule. Fo
example, if a point on the tracing is in the middle c
any one rectangle, its new place on the equal-are
graticule will be in the middle of the correspondin
rectangle. Having moved all points in this way, th

CONSTRUCTION OF DIFFICULT CASES

final network—the zenithal equal-area—can be traced off or pricked through by joining up with curves the points thus plotted.

Fig. 78.—Zenithal Equal-area Map of the Western Hemisphere.

This result could have been obtained similarly by the use of the orthographic projection, or if the whole hemisphere were not required, by the use of the gnomonic. However, trial will soon show that the compression in the one case and expansion in the other render these projections very unsuitable. The stereographic is far and away the best.

In many atlases—notably Diercke—maps of larg
areas are often shown on the zenithal equal-area projec
tion when the plane of the projection is oblique. Tha
is to say, the plane on which the projection is made
not tangent to the Earth at the Equator or Poles, bu
at some point between them. This is a more difficu
case. A glance at any such map will show that bot
meridians and parallels are curves and not arcs of circle

By means of the oblique gnomonic projection th
oblique equal-area network can be obtained. It
rather a tedious process and needs care.

The steps are similar to those in the case alread
described. First, make an oblique gnomonic (page 12
on the required plane and scale. Next, make a series o
circles with radii equal to the distances of the paralle
from the centre of the map. (In Plate III, C is th
centre of the map, and the radii referred to are th
distances C to 50° N., C to 60° N., etc., along the 100t
meridian.) From the common centre of these circle
draw radii at intervals corresponding to the intervals o
longitude on the required map. It is important to not
that these radii and circles do not represent a projectio
and are only a means of obtaining the final result.

Having made this network, place it over the origin
gnomonic projection so that their centres coincide and als
the central meridian of the gnomonic coincides with an
radius of the other. Then mark through the points o
intersection of meridians and parallels as before. (If th
circles do not cover all the area required, more can b
drawn at radii equal to the next succeeding radii o
the gnomonic projection, if that were made to include
greater area.)

Next make a polar zenithal equal-area graticule o

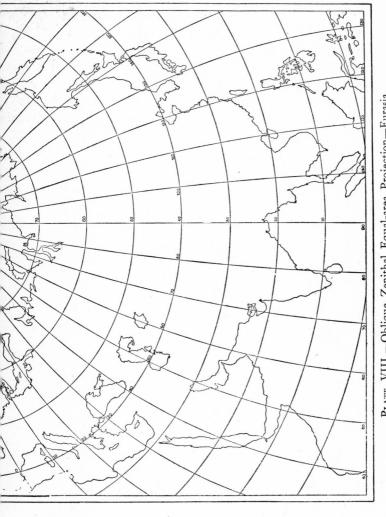

PLATE VIII.—Oblique Zenithal Equal-area Projection—Eurasia.

the same scale and transpose on to it the points o intersection marked on the temporary graticule.

Finally, join up these points, and an equal-area networ is obtained. In this case, however, great care must b taken in marking the new positions of the points, becaus the spacing of the set of circles renders the process rathe difficult.

Similarly, equatorial and oblique graticules can b constructed for other projections—ϵ.g. Sir H. James' Airy's, Clarke's, etc.

CHAPTER VIII

METHOD OF CONSTRUCTING AITOFF'S PROJECTION FROM THE EQUATORIAL ZENITHAL EQUAL-AREA PROJECTION

THE method here employed is that given in Hinks's *Map Projections*. A zenithal equal-area projection of a hemisphere is constructed as for a point on the Equator. A plane making an angle of 60° with the projection is

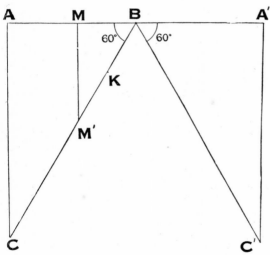

FIG. 79.—Construction of Aitoff's Projection.

then passed through the central meridian on the map. Consequently, if a point on the zenithal equal-area projection be projected vertically from the Equator on to this plane, it will be twice as far from the central meridian it was formerly.

165

In fig. 79 let ABA' be the Equator of the zenitha
equal-area projection, and BC and BC' two plane
making angles of 60° with it. Let M be any poin
on the Equator; M' is its position on the plane BC
if projected vertically from AA. But by trigonometry
BM' = BM sec 60°: and as sec 60° = 2·0000, it follow
that BM' = 2BM; similarly for any other point so
projected.

But the length of the central meridian on the
equal-area projection and on the subsequent Aitof
remains the same. Hence parallels of latitude are
spaced similarly on the central meridian of each
projection.

However, by measurement from the Equator and
from the central meridian the co-ordinates of any poin
on the zenithal equal-area projection are easily found
If we call the central meridian the y axis, and the Equato
the x axis, we can define points on the zenithal equal
area projection. To build the Aitoff, double the
co-ordinate and maintain the y co-ordinate unaltered
the origin being the intersection of the two axes. Then
by joining corresponding points, meridians and parallel
can be drawn in.

The projection is an equal-area projection—th
mode of projection from an equal-area graticule has no
affected this property. This can be seen in part from
the previous diagram. Suppose M were in 50° W. long
Then call M', the projection of M, 100° W. Thus by
halving the scale in longitude—i.e. making K[1](KB = KM'
50° W.—and keeping the latitude scale constant, th
projection remains equal-area.

---

[1] K on final map corresponds to M on equal-area map.

CONSTRUCTING AITOFF'S PROJECTION

This projection has one advantage over the somewhat similar Mollweide—that the parallels and the meridians are curves, and so the intersection angles between parallels and meridians are not so greatly distorted toward the edges of the map. It is very suitable for World maps, especially for those showing distributions. At present it is not common in British atlases, but is frequently found in Continental atlases

CHAPTER IX

THE PARABOLIC AND RELATED PROJECTIONS

This new and interesting projection of the whole sphere was designed by Colonel Craster, who first described it in the *Geographical Journal* (Vol. 74, 1929, p. 471). The construction of the projection involves, perhaps, rather more mathematical knowledge than is assumed in this book, but the main principles of the construction are comparatively simple.

It is an equal-area projection, and is intermediate between the Sinusoidal and the Mollweide projections. The parallels are straight lines, and the meridians are parabolas. The distortion in Polar and Temperate latitudes is less than in Mollweide because the meridians and parallels do not intersect at such acute angles, and the shape is far more pleasing than the Sinusoidal. It is a projection which may, therefore, be used for world maps showing distributions, and it is to be hoped that it will come into use in ordinary atlases (see Plate X).

In fig. 80, CP represents half the central meridian of the projection, and EC half of the Equator.

Hence, CP = 90° of latitude
and EC = 180° of longitude along the Equator = 2 CP. EQP is a parabola representing the meridian 180° from CP.

The equation for a parabola is $y^2 = ax$, where a is a constant to be determined.

PARABOLIC AND RELATED PROJECTIONS

EC is the x axis ; ES the y axis.

For simplicity, take the length CP as one unit of length.

Then, at the point P, $x = 2$ and $y = 1$.

So to satisfy the equation $y^2 = ax$, we must have $a = \frac{1}{2}$;

$$y^2 = \frac{x}{2} ; \quad x = 2y^2.$$

Thus the curve EQP can be plotted by giving arbitrary values to y and calcula-ing the corresponding values for x.

The area EQPC on the projection must be made equal to one quarter of the area of the whole sphere, i.e. πR^2, where R is the radius of the sphere.

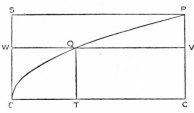

FIG. 80.—Method of constructing the Parabolic Projection.

Since the curve EQP is a parabola, the area of EQPC is $\frac{2}{3}$ of the rectangle ESPC

$$\text{or } \frac{2}{3} \text{ EC} \times \text{PC.}$$

But EC = 2PC, and PC = 1 unit.

$$\therefore \text{ area EQPC} = \frac{4}{3}.$$

But the corresponding area on the sphere is πR^2.

$$\therefore \pi R^2 = \frac{4}{3} \quad . \quad . \quad . \quad (1) \quad \text{and } R = \frac{2}{\sqrt{3\pi}}.$$

$$\therefore R = 0.65147 \times \text{PC units.}$$

Values of PC can be determined from this equation for any given value of R.

The next step is to determine the distances of the parallels from the Equator.

Take any point Q, whose latitude is ϕ. The area EQVC must be made equal to the corresponding area on the sphere.

Area EQT is $\frac{2}{3}$ area ET $\times$ QT $= \frac{2}{3} xy$, where x and y are the co-ordinates of the point Q.

The area of the rectangle TQVC is TC $\times$ VC

$$= (EC - ET) \times VC$$
$$= (2 - x)y$$
$$= 2y - xy.$$

Therefore the area EQVC $= \frac{2}{3} xy + 2y - xy$

$$= 2y - \frac{1}{3} xy$$

$$= 2y - \frac{2}{3} y^3, \text{ since } x = 2y^2.$$

The area of a zone on the sphere is $2\pi R h$,

and $h = R \sin \phi$ (see page 18).

$\therefore$ area of half the zone $= \pi R^2 \sin \phi$.

But $\pi R^2 = \frac{4}{3}$, so the area of half the zone is $\frac{4}{3} \sin \phi$.

By equating the area of EQVC to this we get

$$2y - \frac{2}{3} y^3 = \frac{4}{3} \sin \phi.$$

But $\sin \phi = 3 \sin \frac{\phi}{3} - 4 \sin^3 \frac{\phi}{3}$.

So the equation becomes $2y - \frac{2}{3} y^3 = 4 \sin \frac{\phi}{3} - \frac{16}{3} \sin^3 \frac{\phi}{3}$.

From inspection it will be seen that this equation is satisfied by the value $y = 2 \sin \frac{\phi}{3}$.

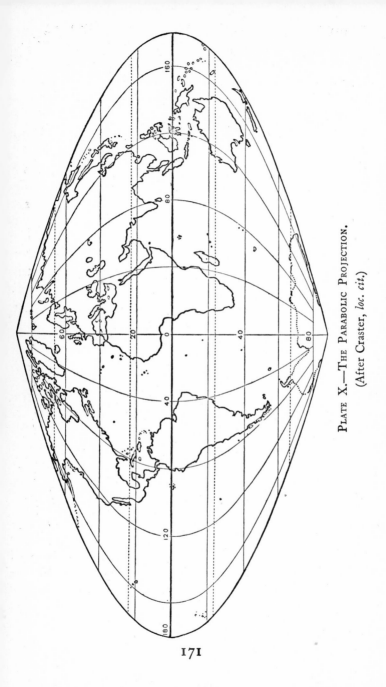

PLATE X.—THE PARABOLIC PROJECTION.

(After Craster, *loc. cit.*)

STUDY OF MAP PROJECTIONS

In this equation y gives the distance from the Equator of any parallel of latitude ϕ. And from the equation $x = 2y^2$ the lengths of each parallel as measured from CP, the central meridian, can be calculated.

These distances and lengths for each $5°$ intervals of latitude are given in the appended table.

To find the positions of the other meridians, divide each parallel into 36 equal parts, and then draw smooth curves through the corresponding points of division on each parallel.

Table showing distances of parallels from the Equator, and the length of each parallel. The length of the Central Meridian, CP, is taken as unity.

Latitude.	Distance from Equator.	Length of parallel measured from Central Meridian.	Latitude.	Distance from Equator.	Length of parallel measured from Central Meridian.
5°	0·058169	1·993233	50°	0·573606	1·341951
10°	0·116290	1·972953	55°	0·629089	1·208493
15°	0·174311	1·939231	60°	0·684040	1·064178
20°	0·232186	1·892179	65°	0·738412	0·909492
25°	0·289864	1·831958	70°	0·792160	0·744966
30°	0·347296	1·758770	75°	0·845237	0·571150
35°	0·404435	1·672864	80°	0·897599	0·388634
40°	0·461232	1·574530	85°	0·949201	0·198035
45°	0·517638	1·464102	90°	1·000000	0·000000

The Parabolic Projection is one of a series. The simplest equal-area projection of the whole sphere is the Sinusoidal, but this can be closely imitated if the sine curve is replaced by a hyperbola. No attempt will be made here to describe an example of the Hyperbolic projections : they are referred to because they form the first group of Craster's series. In any case, the Sinusoidal will usually be preferred to them, because it is simpler to construct. The reader is referred to the table on page 176 which indicates the spacing of the parallels on certain selected types of this series of projections, including the case of the Hyperbolic which is nearest to the Sinusoidal. The spacing of the meridians on these projections is referred to below.

The Parabolic Projection forms the second group of the series. By decreasing the eccentricity of the hyperbola, and making it unity, the particular case of the parabolic already described is obtained.

By a still further decrease in the eccentricity, the curves become ellipses. Mollweide's Projection, described in Chapter V, may be taken as an illustration of this group and forms the last of the series. An Elliptical Projection (see table, p. 176) can also be constructed to imitate the Eumorphic Projection, of which an account is given below.

In all these projections, Hyperbolic, Parabolic, and Elliptical, all the meridians, in every case, are like curves. " Thus, all the meridians in the hyperbolic projections are hyperbolas, in the parabolic projection they are parabolas, and in the elliptical projection they are ellipses. In all these projections the parallels are truly divided, and the meridians may therefore be drawn as smooth curves through the points of division " (Craster, *loc. cit.*).

If, on the other hand, the eccentricity of the Hyperbolic projection is made infinitely great, the hyperbola becomes two straight lines, and the projection is rectilinear. Whilst such a projection is easy to draw, it possesses no real merit.

In the *Geographical Journal* (March 1929), Whittemore Boggs described an equal-area projection of the whole sphere which he called the Eumorphic Projection (Plate XI). It is an arithmetical mean between the

Sinusoidal and Mollweide (fig. 81). For example, in computing the 90th meridian from the centre in this projection, the first step is to take the arithmetic mean between the Sinusoidal and Mollweide graticules for each parallel of latitude. A formula is then derived for *x*

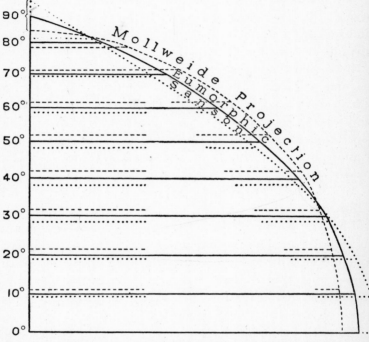

FIG. 81.—Relations between the Eumorphic, Sinusoidal, and Mollweide Projections. (After Whittemore Boggs, *loc. cit.*)

(i.e. east-west distances) so that strict equality of area is maintained, i.e. the area enclosed by the curve is precisely the same as that enclosed by the corresponding curves on the Sinusoidal and Mollweide networks. In this way the following table is obtained for plotting the 90th meridian from a sphere of unit radius :

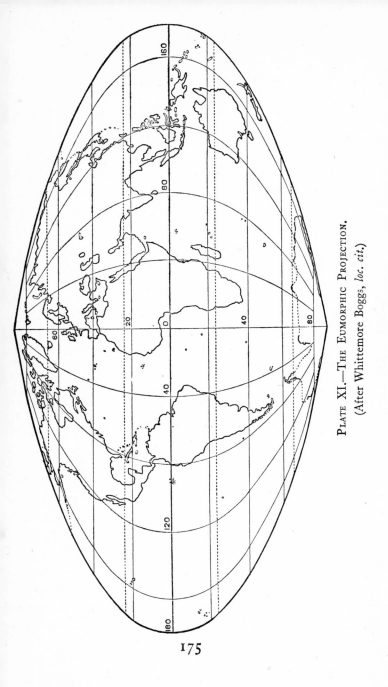

PLATE XI.—THE EUMORPHIC PROJECTION.

(After Whittemore Boggs, *loc. cit.*)

175

	x	y			x	y
Lat. 0	1·490450	0·000000	Lat. 50		1·041960	0·895537
,, 10	1·472335	0·183753	,, 60		0·846496	1·061226
,, 20	1·418091	0·366372	,, 70		0·615121	1·218648
,, 30	1·328006	0·546698	,, 80		0·343191	1·364746
,, 40	1·202494	0·723524	,, 90		0·000000	1·490450

By this means the serious inequality of linear scale so conspicuous near the Equator on Mollweide, reduced. Similarly, the linear scales in the zone betwee 60° and 75° are improved. Angular distortion is also le in this projection than it is in the Sinusoidal below 62 but it exceeds that of Mollweide because it is not possibl in this projection to improve on both the inequality o linear scales and angular distortion at the same tim Above 62°, however, the angular error in this projectio is less than in Mollweide. This projection also len itself to " interruption."

TABLE GIVING DISTANCES OF THE PARALLELS FROM TH EQUATOR ON CERTAIN PROJECTIONS

Lat.	Sanson.	Hyperbolic nearest Sanson.	Parabolic.	Eumorphic.	Elliptical nearest Eumorphic.	Mollweide
10°	0·1111	0·1112	0·1163	0·1234	0·1233	0·1368
20°	0·2222	0·2224	0·2322	0·2458	0·2456	0·2720
30°	0·3333	0·3338	0·3473	0·3668	0·3662	0·4040
40°	0·4444	0·4454	0·4612	0·4854	0·4840	0·5310
50°	0·5556	0·5571	0·5736	0·6009	0·5982	0·6512
60°	0·6667	0·6688	0·6840	0·7119	0·7079	0·7624
70°	0·7778	0·7800	0·7921	0·8177	0·8122	0·8620
80°	0·8889	0·8906	0·8976	0·9159	0·9099	0·9454
90°	1·0000	1·0000	1·0000	1·0000	1·0000	1·0000
R	0·63662	0·63662	0·65147	0·67094	0·67094	0·70711

(After Craster, *loc. cit.*)

Amongst all of these projections Mollweide has on feature peculiar to it. It is the only one in which th

ıeridian curves pass continuously through the Poles.
n all the others there is a break, or discontinuity, at these
oints.   Conventionally, this may be a reason for pre-
erring the Mollweide, but we are, perhaps, all too con-
ervative in our atlases.   It would be a very good thing if
greater variety of projections came into everyday use.

CHAPTER X

OTHER CONICAL PROJECTIONS

THERE are several other conical projections which ar
of some interest but which are not used very much
The simplest is the *Conical Equal-area with One Standar
Parallel*. In this projection the pole of the cone and th
pole of the Earth are coincident. As in all conical
the scale on the parallels is incorrect except on th
standard parallel.

The conical equal-area is so modified that the meridia
scale is incorrect in inverse proportion to the latitud
scale. The parallels are not equally spaced, and ar
farther apart on the poleward side of the standar
parallel and nearer together on the equatorial side
Thus exaggeration takes place in a north and sout
direction on the one side and in an east and west directio
on the other side of the standard parallel. For thi
reason it is not of any great use.

This projection is often called Lambert's Conica
Equal-area Projection.

There are two ways of approaching its construction
It may be derived directly from the Simple Conic, i
which case the apex of the cone will *not* coincide wit
the pole which (as in the simple conic) will be an ar
whose length will depend upon the parallel chosen a
standard. Or, the projection may be so made that th
apex of the cone and the pole will coincide. Case

resolves itself into the problem of representing the area of a *zone* or *belt* of a sphere on a cone. (See pp. 15 and 16 *et seq.*)

Let n be the constant of the cone and suppose r_0 is the radius of any parallel of latitude drawn on the cone, with the apex as centre.

Then the area on the cone bounded by that parallel is $n\pi r_0^2$.

If r_1 is any other parallel, then the area bounded by it is $n\pi r_1^2$,

∴ the strip round the cone bounded by these parallels is :

$$n\pi r_0^2 - n\pi r_1^2 = n\pi(r_0^2 - r_1^2)$$

On page 18, the area of a zone or belt on the sphere was shown to be $2\pi R^2 \sin \phi$ where ϕ represents the latitude of the bounding parallel.

If two parallels, ϕ_0 and ϕ_1, be taken, then the area of the enclosed strip is :

$$2\pi R^2 \sin \phi_0 - 2\pi R^2 \sin \phi_1 = 2\pi R^2 (\sin \phi_0 - \sin \phi_1).$$

Hence, in order to make the projection equal area, the areas on the cone and the sphere must be equated :

$$n\pi (r_0^2 - r_1^2) = 2\pi R^2 (\sin \phi_0 - \sin \phi_1).$$

But n, the constant of the cone, in the simple conic $= \sin \phi$ (see page 72), and r_0 the radius of the standard parallel $= R \cot \phi_0$. Substituting these values in the equation given above, we have :

$$\pi \sin \phi_0 (R^2 \cot^2 \phi_0 - r_1^2) = 2\pi R^2 (\sin \phi_0 - \sin \phi_1)$$

and $\sin \phi_0 (R^2 \cot^2 \phi_0 - r_1^2) = 2R^2 \sin \phi_0 - 2R^2 \sin \phi_1.$

Dividing both sides by $\sin \phi_0$ we have :

$$R^2 \cot^2 \phi_0 - r_1^2 = 2R^2 - \frac{2R^2 \sin \phi_1}{\sin \phi_0}$$

$$\therefore \quad r_1^2 = R^2 \cot^2 \phi_0 - 2R^2 + \frac{2R^2 \sin \phi_1}{\sin \phi_0}$$

$$\text{and} \quad r_1 = \sqrt{R^2 \cot^2 \phi_0 - 2R^2 + \frac{2R^2 \sin \phi_1}{\sin \phi_0}}$$

From this equation the radius of any other parallel can be found.

Case II. The problem in this case turns upon obtaining an equation between the area of a *segment* of a sphere and part (or all) of a cone.

The area of the segment of a sphere is the area of a great circle multiplied by the altitude of the segment (page 18).

Therefore area $= 2\pi R \times (R - R \sin \phi)$

$$= 2\pi R^2 (1 - \sin \phi).$$

But $1 - \sin \phi = 1 - \cos \chi$

$$= 1 - (1 - 2 \sin^2 \tfrac{1}{2}\chi)$$

(since $\cos 2A = 1 - 2 \sin^2 A$)

$$= 2 \sin^2 \tfrac{1}{2}\chi.$$

Therefore whole area of segment

$$= 2\pi R^2 \times 2 \sin^2 \tfrac{1}{2}\chi$$

$$= 4\pi R^2 \times \sin^2 \tfrac{1}{2}\chi.$$

But the corresponding area of a cone $= n\pi r^2$, where n is the constant of the cone.

Thus we obtain the following equation :

$$n\pi r^2 = 4\pi R^2 \sin^2 \tfrac{1}{2}\chi . \qquad . \qquad . \qquad . \quad (1$$

The projection, however, is to have one parallel correct to scale. Call this parallel ϕ_0.

The length of such a parallel on the globe is $2\pi R \cos \phi_0$.

And the length of the same parallel on the cone or on the projection is $2\pi r_0 n$.

Equating these expressions, we have :

$$2\pi r_0 n = 2\pi R \cos \phi_0$$

$$\text{and} \quad n r_0 = R \cos \phi_0$$

$$= R \sin \chi_0$$

$$= 2R \sin \tfrac{1}{2}\chi_0 \cos \tfrac{1}{2}\chi_0 \qquad . \qquad . \quad (2$$

If now we divide (1) by (2) we have * :

$$\frac{n\pi r_0{}^2}{n r_0} = \frac{4\pi R^2 \sin^2 \frac{1}{2}\chi_0}{2R \sin \frac{1}{2}\chi_0 \cos \frac{1}{2}\chi_0}$$

$$\text{and } r_0 = \frac{4R^2 \sin^2 \frac{1}{2}\chi_0}{2R \sin \frac{1}{2}\chi_0 \cos \frac{1}{2}\chi_0}$$

$$= \frac{2R \sin \frac{1}{2}\chi_0}{\cos \frac{1}{2}\chi_0}$$

$$= 2R \tan \frac{1}{2}\chi_0 \ . \qquad . \qquad . \qquad . \quad (3)$$

We have to find n by substituting (3) in (2) :

$$n = \frac{2R \sin \frac{1}{2}\chi_0 \cos \frac{1}{2}\chi_0 \cos \frac{1}{2}\chi_0}{2R \sin \frac{1}{2}\chi_0}$$

$$= \cos^2 \frac{1}{2}\chi_0.$$

Finally, to find a general expression for the radius of any parallel substitute in (1) :

$$\cos^2 \frac{1}{2}\chi_0 \ r^2\pi = 4\pi R^2 \sin^2 \frac{1}{2}\chi$$

$$r^2 = 4R^2 \sin^2 \frac{1}{2}\chi \sec^2 \frac{1}{2}\chi_0$$

$$r = 2R \sin \frac{1}{2}\chi \sec \frac{1}{2}\chi_0$$

Albers' Conical Equal-area has two standard parallels. The construction is more difficult. The apex of the cone and the pole of the Earth are no longer coincident; the pole on the projection is represented by an arc of finite length. Both meridian and parallel scales are in inverse proportion to one another in order that the projection may be equal-area. Between the two standard parallels the scale along the meridians is too large, outside them it is too small, and this defect increases with distance from the standard parallels.

* $r = r_0.$
  $\chi = \chi_0.$
  $\phi = \phi_0$, where $\phi_0 =$ standard parallel
  $\chi_0 =$ co-latitude of the standard parallel
  and $r_0 =$ radius of the standard parallel on the projection.

The following means of construction may be found useful :

Let ϕ_1 and ϕ_2 be the latitudes of the two standard parallels ; r_1 and r_2 be their radii on the projection,* and n be the constant of the cone. It is necessary first of all to find n in terms of ϕ_1 and ϕ_2.

The area of the strip of a cone between the circles representing latitudes ϕ_1 and ϕ_2 is :

$$n\pi r_1^2 - n\pi r_2^2 = n\pi (r_1^2 - r_2^2)$$

The area of the zone of a sphere between two parallels ϕ_1 and ϕ_2 is :

$$2\pi R^2 \sin \phi_2 - 2\pi R^2 \sin \phi_1 = 2\pi R^2 (\sin \phi_2 - \sin \phi_1)$$

Hence for the projection to be equal area :

$$n\pi (r_1^2 - r_2^2) = 2\pi R^2 (\sin \phi_2 - \sin \phi_1) \quad . \quad . \quad . \quad (1)$$

On the projection the lengths of the parallels ϕ_1 and ϕ_2 will be :

$$n2\pi r_1 \text{ and } n2\pi r_2$$

These are standard parallels and must be their true length, thus :

$$n2\pi r_1 = 2\pi R \cos \phi_1 \text{ and } n2\pi r_2 = 2\pi R \cos \phi_2$$

$$\therefore r_1 = \frac{R \cos \phi_1}{n} \text{ and } r_2 = \frac{R \cos \phi_2}{n} \quad . \quad . \quad . \quad (2)$$

By substituting these values in equation (1) we have :

$$n\pi \left(\frac{R^2 \cos^2 \phi_1}{n^2} - \frac{R^2 \cos^2 \phi_2}{n^2}\right) = 2\pi R^2 (\sin \phi_2 - \sin \phi_1)$$

and $\dfrac{R^2 \cos^2 \phi_1 - R^2 \cos^2 \phi_2}{n} = 2R^2 (\sin \phi_2 - \sin \phi_1)$

* If ϕ_2 represents a higher latitude than ϕ_1 then r_2 is less than r_1.

$$\therefore \quad n = \frac{\cos^2 \phi_1 - \cos^2 \phi_2}{2 (\sin \phi_2 - \sin \phi_1)}$$

$$= \frac{1 - \sin^2 \phi_1 - (1 - \sin^2 \phi_2)}{2 (\sin \phi_2 - \sin \phi_1)}$$

$$= \frac{- \sin^2 \phi_1 + \sin^2 \phi_2}{2 (\sin \phi_2 - \sin \phi_1)}$$

$$= \frac{\sin^2 \phi_2 - \sin^2 \phi_1}{2 (\sin \phi_2 - \sin \phi_1)}$$

$$= \frac{(\sin \phi_2 - \sin \phi_1)(\sin \phi_2 + \sin \phi_1)}{2 (\sin \phi_2 - \sin \phi_1)}$$

$$= \tfrac{1}{2} (\sin \phi_2 + \sin \phi_1)$$

Substituting the value for n in equation (2), we have:

$$r_1 = \frac{R \cos \phi_1}{\tfrac{1}{2} (\sin \phi_1 + \sin \phi_2)} \quad \text{and} \quad r_2 = \frac{R \cos \phi_2}{\tfrac{1}{2} (\sin \phi_1 + \sin \phi_2)}$$

To find the radius of any other parallel—say ϕ_3—we have:

$$\text{area on map} \quad = n\pi (r_3^2 - r_1^2)$$
$$\text{area on sphere} = 2\pi R^2 (\sin \phi_1 - \sin \phi_3)$$

Hence $n\pi r_3^2 - n\pi r_1^2 = 2\pi R^2 (\sin \phi_1 - \sin \phi_3)$

and $n r_3^2 = n r_1^2 + 2R^2 (\sin \phi_1 - \sin \phi_3)$

$$\therefore \quad r_3^2 = \frac{n r_1^2 + 2R^2 (\sin \phi_1 - \sin \phi_3)}{n}$$

and $\quad r_3 = \sqrt{\dfrac{n r_1^2 + 2R^2 (\sin \phi_1 - \sin \phi_3)}{n}}$

The *Conical Orthomorphic Projection* may have one or two standard parallels. Neither case is in common use. The problem is to make the meridian and the parallel scales the same at any point on the map. The calculation is not easy. As in all conicals, the scale on the standard parallel or parallels is correct. The scale on the other parallels is too great, but it is clearly an advantage to have the scale correct along two parallels if possible. For this reason the conical orthomorphic with two standard parallels (*Lambert's Second or Gauss's* is the more common).[1] If two parallels are standard, the scale along the intermediate parallels is too small, and on the outside parallels too great.

All conicals have two advantages in common :

(1) Meridians and parallels are at right angles, and

(2) Apart from calculations they are very easy to draw.

[1] The conical orthomorphic projection with two standard parallels is used in Debes's Atlas.

CHAPTER XI

THIS map, of international importance, is constructed on a modified form of the polyconic projection. In the ordinary polyconic the meridians were curves obtained by passing lines through a series of points on the parallels. In the International Map the meridians are straight lines. The parallels are arcs of circles whose centres are situated on the central meridian produced. There are many projections which differ very little from one another, and it was found that within the limits of the individual sheets of the International Map it was better to discard absolute equivalence of area or exact orthomorphism in favour of a projection which lent itself to easy construction and which enabled adjoining sheets to fit one another correctly. These conditions were found to be satisfied by modifying the ordinary polyconic so that the meridians were straight lines.

Each sheet of the map is plotted quite independently on its own central meridian, and this meridian is a straight line. The top and bottom parallels of a given sheet are arcs of circles, and their centres are on the prolongation of the central meridian. These two parallels are constructed from tables. As in the ordinary polyconic, the parallels of latitude are not concentric arcs. Having drawn in the top and bottom parallels of a given sheet (these two parallels correspond to the north and south

185

STUDY OF MAP PROJECTIONS

edges of the sheet), divide them truly as if they were
ordinary parallels on the unmodified polyconic. Then
join points on these two parallels by straight lines to
represent the meridians. One further modification is
made. In the simple polyconic the only meridian true
to scale is the central meridian. In the International
Map two meridians on each sheet are correct. These
meridians are 2° E. and W. of the central meridian
of each sheet respectively. In order to make these

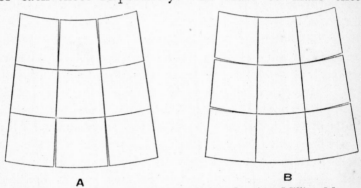

A   B

Fig. 82.—Arrangement of Sheets on the One-in-a-Million Map.

correct, it follows that the central meridian must no
longer remain true to scale.

In this way the parallels of the sheet are, as it were,
shifted toward one another so that they become their
true distance apart along the two meridians instead of
along the centre one. The scale along the central
meridian is thus too small.

By this method of construction it is possible to make
adjoining sheets[1] fit. If a series of nine neighbouring
sheets (arranged as in the figs. 82a and 82b) are con-

[1] Each sheet covers 4° of latitude and 6° of longitude, and in latitude
higher than 60°, 12° of longitude.

idered, it will be seen that while it is impossible to make all fit exactly, they can be so arranged that those bordering one another along their east and west margins will fit, because these sheets are drawn on the same radii; and also sheets north and south of one another will fit along their common margin. It is clear that if more sheets than nine are used, it is not possible to join them with any pretence to accuracy.

The great merits of the International Map projection are, then, that it is easy to construct, and, because each sheet is complete within itself, it is a relatively simple matter to make tables to cover all possible cases. Further, within the limits of a single sheet the effects of contraction and expansion of the paper are sufficient to outweigh an exact equivalence of area or true orthomorphism, so that any sheet may be considered as approximately fulfilling both these conditions, at any rate for all practical purposes.

PART 2. ORDNANCE SURVEY MAPS

PROJECTION ON CASSINI'S RECTANGULAR CO-ORDINATE SYSTEM

This is in part a form of cylindrical projection: the cylinder is supposed tangent to the globe along the central meridian of the area to be mapped. In order to make the map, first choose a central meridian and fix on some point—X—for the centre of the map. In order to find the position of any other point, say Y, the following process is employed. From Y suppose a great circle be drawn perpendicular to the central meridian, and let it meet it at K. Now calculate the lengths of YK and XK on the Earth's surface. This is done by means of spherical trigonometry, and then the distance YK and XK are plotted directly. In other words, the great-circle distances YK and XK (fig. 83) are represented on the map by two straight lines (to scale) at right angles to one another—they are, in fact, the rectangular co-ordinates of the point Y on a plane. Each point of intersection of meridian and parallel is so plotted on one large sheet. The sheet is then cut up into conveniently sized parts. Because all these parts fit together to make one sheet, the sheets fit one another along their edges.

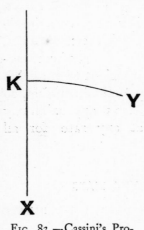

FIG. 83.—Cassini's Projection.

In the case of Great Britain the errors which are, of necessity, introduced are not too great. On any one of the single sheets the curvature of the meridian is not noticeable. The central meridian is true to scale, but the other meridians are too long ; in other words, scale north and south is exaggerated on all but the central meridian. This can be seen quite easily : the central meridian is a straight line correctly divided. The other meridians are lines passed through a series of points on the parallels, and plotted by rectangular co-ordinates. As the distance between meridians decreases polewards, the meridians on the map are curved, and therefore longer than the central meridian. The fact that the meridians are curved is in itself a disadvantage. The separate sheets of the Ordnance Survey, however, are rectangular, therefore their edges are not parallel.

with the meridians. The deviation of the sheet edge from the meridian increases with distance from the central meridian and may reach as much as 4°. Both the 1-inch map of England and the 6-inch map of the United Kingdom are plotted on this projection.

CHAPTER XII

In recent years a good deal of interest has been taken i
projections. The Parabolic and related graticules hav
already been described, but in the following notes n
attempt will be made to explain the mathematical con
structions involved in the projections described. How
ever, in a book of this sort, some brief descriptions seer
to be called for. Although a few of these projections ar
special cases of those already described, it seems best t
include them in this chapter rather than to add them a
notes after the normal cases. The student is not the
worried by unnecessary detail, and can concentrate on th
more usual developments. If the reader is interested i
obtaining further details, he can consult the origina
sources which are given in brackets :

THE TRANSVERSE MOLLWEIDE

The Transverse Mollweide is so made that the Equato
of the normal case becomes the central meridian of th
transverse case, and the Poles are, therefore, turnec
through an angle of 90°.

The normal case of this projection has been describec
in detail, and its merits and demerits mentioned. Th
transverse case gives a good representation of the land:
around the Poles, but the Equator of the projection under-
goes a sudden change, forming not only the boundary o

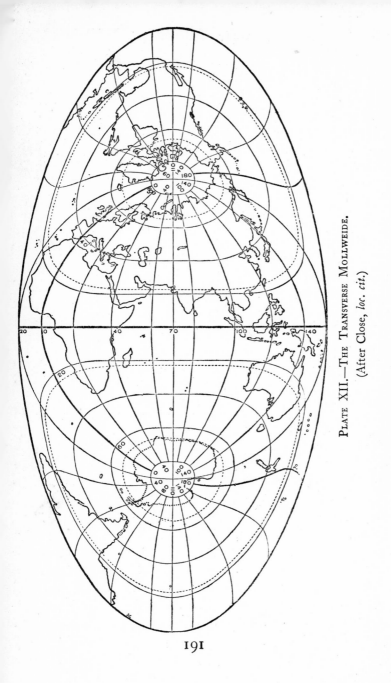

PLATE XII.—THE TRANSVERSE MOLLWEIDE.

(After Close, *loc. cit.*)

191

the graticule, but also the horizontal straight line throug]
the centre. Neither parallels nor meridians are simpl
curves, but the property of equivalence of area is main
tained. If a suitable meridian is chosen, the Britis]
Empire is well portrayed. (See Plate XII.) (For detai]
see *Ordnance Survey Professional Paper*, 1927.)

THE OBLIQUE MOLLWEIDE

The first description of the oblique case was given by]
Fairgrieve (*Geography*, Autumn 1928, p. 528), who trie
to solve the problem of how best to show the Britis]
Empire on one sheet so as to bring out the followin
essential facts : (*a*) The " axis " of the Empire as a grea
circle from the Bahamas to New Zealand ; (*b*) the import
ance of strategic positions near this axis; and (*c*) th
comparative strategical importance of the exterior land:
To do this he used a Mollweide Projection, in which th
ends of the minor axis are situated in latitudes 45° N
and S., and the particular map he drew had these point
fixed in N. lat. 45° and E. long. 150°, and S. lat. 45
and W. long. 30°. Through these points, or any othe
pair, an infinite number of such projections can b
drawn, but for the purpose Fairgrieve had in view, th
most suitable was that in which the minor axis is th
great circle passing through the Equator and 48° E
long.

This projection was later investigated by Sir Charle
Close (*Geogr. Journ.*, 73, 1929, p. 251), who also com
puted the co-ordinates of a graticule with 30° interval
between parallels and meridians. As a result of hi
investigation, Close found :

(1) " The old central circle remains a meridian on th

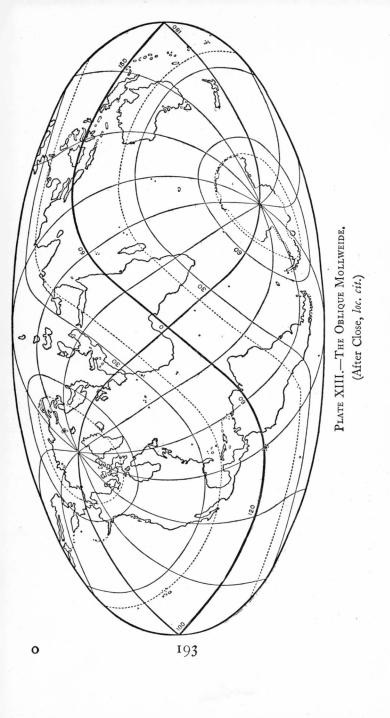

PLATE XIII.—THE OBLIQUE MOLLWEIDE.

(After Close, *loc. cit.*)

new projection, and it is the meridian 90° from th[e]
"principal meridian" (see Plate XIII).

(2) "The principal meridian may be defined as th[at]
which passes through the centre of the bounding ellipse[;]
this principal meridian and the Equator of the ne[w]
projection are similar curves, inverted with respect to eac[h]
other, each passing through the centre of the ellipse an[d]
each terminating at the ends of the major axis."

(3) "The new parallels of 0°, 30°, and 60° north touc[h]
the old parallels of 45° north and south, 15° south an[d]
75° north, and 15° north and 75° south; and similar[ly]
with the southern parallels" (loc cit., page 251). F[or]
further details the reader is referred to the paper cite[d.]

THE TRANSVERSE MERCATOR

In the ordinary development of the Mercator Pr[o]
jection, the cylinder on which the projection is ma[de]
touches the globe along the Equator. In the tran[s]
verse case the cylinder touches the globe along a[r]
meridian. In fig. 84 the relation of a Transverse Mercat[or]
to a normal case is shown, the latter being turned throug[h]
90° in azimuth. Thus, the meridians of the normal ca[se]
appear as horizontal straight lines and the parallels [as]
vertical lines. It will be noticed also that the vertic[al]
meridian of the transverse case is the Equator of th[e]
normal projection. Further, the numbers of the ne[w]
meridians are the complements of the numbers of th[e]
parallels in the original graticule: the same relatio[n]
holds between the parallels in the transverse case and th[e]
meridians in the normal. The new projection [is]
symmetrical about the Equator on the Central Meridia[n.]
Special tables have been drawn up to enable the rap[id]

194

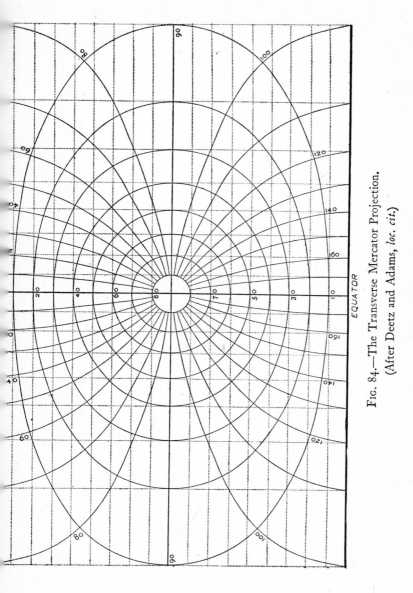

FIG. 84.—The Transverse Mercator Projection.
(After Deetz and Adams, *loc. cit.*)

plotting of this projection. (See *Special Publicatio No. 67, U.S. Coast and Geodetic Survey*, and also C. F Deetz and O. S. Adams, " Elements of Map Projection, *U.S. Coast and Geodetic Survey, Special Publication No. 68* 1921.)

The Transverse Mercator has, of recent years, becom of increasing importance as a projection for topographica maps of comparatively small areas, for which alone it used. Those colonies which use this projection choos two or more standard meridians, so that the distortio is reduced to a minimum, even at the expense of a lack fit between sheets. It is the orthomorphic form of th Cassini projection.

RETRO-AZIMUTHAL PROJECTIONS

Ordinary azimuthal projections give true azimuths fro the centre of the map. Retro-azimuthal Projections, o the other hand, give the azimuth of the centre from an point. There are clearly certain advantages in suc projections, but from the point of view of the geograph they are perhaps of interest rather than of real value.

The Mecca Retro-Azimuthal Projection was fir described by J. I. Craig (*Survey Department, Map Pr jections, Cairo*, 1909), and it enables a map to be draw which gives the true bearing of Mecca from every poi on the map. Craig made his meridians equidista parallel straight lines, correctly spaced on the Equato or in the latitude of Mecca. The straight line on th map from any place to Mecca is not the projection of loxodrome, and, further, the parallels generally do n intersect the meridians at right angles. Consequentl azimuths must be measured from the meridian lin But Craig's projection cannot be extended to include emisphere, and the Stereographic, which is also retro-zimuthal (see A. R. Hinks, *Geogr. Journ.*, 73, 1929, page 45), cannot include the whole sphere. Further, in this class of projections, retro-azimuths must be measured from the tangent to the curved meridian through the point.

E. A. Reeves (*Geogr. Journ.*, 73, 1929, page 247) has given a short description of a chart in which the bearing of Rugby can be read off, for all parts of the world. Reeves took as his basis an Admiralty Mercator Chart of the world on which he drew curves of Equal Reverse Azimuth from Rugby. The resulting chart bore some similarity to a chart showing lines of equal magnetic variation for the world. All places on a given curve have the same true bearing to Rugby. The curves are drawn at 5° intervals, and are reckoned always from the north, east or west, up to 180°. Reeves has also published a " True Bearing and Distance Diagram " (in *R.G.S. Technical Series, No.* 3). From this diagram it is possible to obtain the bearing of any place on the earth from any other place, and this diagram was used in the construction of the Rugby chart. Similar charts can be made for any other place.

Reeves's " Rugby Diagram " was made the basis of an interesting and somewhat amusing investigation by A. R. Hinks (*Geogr. Journ.*, 73, 1929, page 245), who constructed a retro-azimuthal projection for the whole sphere. Rugby was chosen as the centre of this projection, though another was made with Malabar as centre (see plates in paper referred to). The result was somewhat extraordinary. The antipodes of Rugby is represented by a circle, with Rugby as centre, bounding the projection. The North and South Poles are con-

centric circles, and there is a large blank area inside th
projection which is no part of it at all! "And what i
more interesting, we have a construction which satisfie
the definition of a map projection, that it will be a
orderly arrangement of meridians and parallels, thougl
upon it one cannot possibly draw a map, because i
parts it is so to speak folded back on itself, and we hav
areas reversed and superposed on others" (Hinks
loc. cit.). Any point can be made the centre of the
projection, but the results are no less astonishing
When, for example, the centre is near the equator, the
circles representing the north and south polar circle
coalesce at half the radius of the antipodal circle
and a straight line of finite length represents th
Equator.

Maurer's Orthodromic, or the Two-Point Azimutha Projection

This is an interesting development obtained from th
ordinary Gnomonic Projection. Until 1922 it wa
believed that the Gnomonic was the only projection o
which great circles could be represented as straight lines
Maurer, however, has shown that the Gnomonic can b
modified by "expansion" or "compression" in an
direction in such a way that all the co-ordinates in tha
direction are altered in a constant ratio. By doing thi
straight lines still remain straight and the main propert
of the normal Gnomonic is unchanged. In this nev
projection not only are there two points at whic.
straight lines represent great circles, but also at whic
azimuths to all other points are correct. Hence, it i
of great value in plotting wireless waves arriving at tw
stations, and for finding the source of the waves (se

Zeit. für Vermessungswesen, January 1922, and also Sir
Charles Close, *Geography*, Summer 1927).

THE TWO-POINT EQUIDISTANT PROJECTION
This interesting projection is due to Sir Charles Close

Fig. 85.—The Two-Point Equidistant Projection of the North Atlantic.
(After Close, *loc. cit.*)

(*Geogr. Journ.*, 57, 1921, page 446).   The main feature
of the projection is that the two straight-line distances
between any arbitrary point and two fixed points are
correct.   If a sailor is plying between, say, Yokohama
and San Francisco, no matter how much he deviates

from his course, he can obtain his true distance from either of those places by direct measurement on the map from his own position to these two fixed points. On the projection the great circle joining the two fixed points is a straight line true to scale. When the Pole is one of the fixed points, the parallels are concentric circles at their true distances apart, and the meridian through the other point is also a straight line true to scale. The other meridians are curved. Fig. 85 shows this projection developed for the North Atlantic, New York and Land's End being the two fixed points.

The general nature of the construction is given by Sir Charles Close as follows : " Select the two points, plot their distance apart as a straight line, true to scale. To find the position on paper of any other point of known latitude and longitude, calculate by spherical or spheroidal methods the distances of this point from the two chosen points. The intersection of these two distances, measured from the two original points, will give the position, on paper, of the new point. The position can also be plotted by co-ordinates " (*Geography*, Summer 1927, page 108).

MODIFICATIONS OF THE POLYCONIC PROJECTION

(a) *The Rectangular Polyconic*

This projection, sometimes called the War Office projection, has its parallels constructed in exactly the same way as those in the ordinary Polyconic, but they are not all divided truly. The Equator is correctly divided, and the meridians are drawn as curves through the appropriate points on this line, and in such a way that they cut the remaining parallels at right angles. Usually meridian distances are too great, and those along the parallels too small. It is never used for more than one sheet of a topographical map, and it is neither orthomorphic nor equal-area.

(b) The Modified Rectangular Polyconic

This is an improvement on the above, and was devised by G. T. McCaw. If a parallel other than the Equator is chosen for correct division, the scale error on the parallels is reduced, but this slight change does not affect the meridian scale. " It then becomes a question whether the scale error on the parallel could be brought up to the scale error on the meridian, thus making the projection orthomorphic; we could then reduce the scale error over the whole map by making use of a scale factor in the ordinary way " (*Geogr. Journ.*, 57, 1921, page 451).

McCaw solved this problem, and so produced a projection which is a rectangular polyconic, and is to all intents and purposes orthomorphic. " The modified projection is suitable for a meridional rather than a longitudinal configuration, but for areas whose total width does not exceed 40° of longitude it seems to be little, if any, inferior to the best forms of representation where the meridional extent is also considerable. The scale error is very much the same as that of the Transverse Mercator (Gauss Conformal). It would form an excellent projection for a general map of Egypt and the Anglo-Egyptian Sudan, or a country of similar proportions " (*loc. cit.*, page 454).

[For further information on Polyconic Projections, see G. T. McCaw, *Internat. Geog. Congr.*, *Cambridge*, 1928, pages 112–117. The possibility of using this Projection for a world map is there discussed.]

APPENDIX I

TABLE OF SUITABLE PROJECTIONS

Use.	Type.	Suitable Projections.
Maps of the World in hemispheres.	1. Equal-area.	Zenithal Equal-area (i.e. Lambert's). Mollweide in hemispheres.
	2. Orthomorphic.	Stereographic.
	3. General.	Zenithal Equidistant. Globular.
Maps of the World in *one* sheet.	1. Equal-area.	Cylindrical Equal-area. [Great east-west distortion near Poles.] Sinusoidal. [Awkward shape; distortion, especially in north and south of the map.] Parabolic. [Intermediate between Sinusoidal and Mollweide as far as shape is concerned.] Eumorphic. [Arithmetical mean between Sinusoidal and Mollweide.] Mollweide.⎫ Aitoff. ⎭ [Especially good for distributions: pleasing shape.]
	2. Orthomorphic.	Mercator. [All bearings correct.]
	3. General.	Gall's Stereographic. [Exaggeration less great than in Mercator; occupies less room.] Van der Grinten's Projection. [Adaptable, but not very suitable.]
	4. Particular Purposes.	Transverse and Oblique Cases of Mollweide. Interrupted Forms of Sinusoidal, Mollweide, Eumorphic. [I.e. Graticules so arranged as to focus attention on certain areas or distributions.]

202

Continental maps:		
A.—Asia and N. America.	1. Equal-area.	Lambert's Zenithal Equal-area (= Lambert's Equal-area Azimuthal). [Bearings true from centre.]
	2. General.	Bonne. [Great distortion in N.E. and N.W. corners.] Zenithal Equidistant. [Bearings true from centre.]
B.—Europe and Australia.	1. Equal-area.	Lambert's Zenithal Equal-area. Bonne. Albers' Conical Equal-area with Two Standard Parallels. Simple Conic with Two Standard Parallels.
	2. General.	Lambert's Zenithal Equal-area.
C.—Africa and S. America.	1. Equal-area.	Sinusoidal (or even Bonne in case of South America). Mollweide. Aitoff. Cylindrical Equal-area. ⎫ [Not usual, but adaptable, especially Aitoff.]
	2. General.	Zenithal Equidistant. Mercator. Stereographic. Orthographic. Globular. ⎬ [Any of these could be used, but no particular advantage would be gained.]
Polar Regions.	1. Equal-area.	Lambert's Zenithal Equal-area. ⎫ A great many projections—e.g. Gnomonic, Stereographic—are fairly suitable, but the two mentioned are probably best.
	2. Equidistant.	Zenithal Equidistant. ⎬

Use.	Type.	Suitable Projections.
Large Countries in Temperate Latitudes—e.g. U.S.A., Russia, China, etc.	1. Equal-area.	Lambert's Zenithal Equal-area. Conical Equal-area with One Standard Parallel. Albers' Conical Equal-area with Two Standard Parallels. Bonne. [The Zenithal Equal-area is suitable for most countries, but as it is difficult to construct, and as no very great advantage is gained by using it for regions of less than continental size, it is more probable that a simpler projection will be used for countries in temperate latitudes.]
	2. General.	Simple Conic with Two Standard Parallels. Conical Orthomorphic with One or Two Standard Parallels. [Debes's Atlas has examples of this projection.]
Large and Small Countries in the Tropics, e.g. India, Brazil, etc.		If the country is cut by the Equator, or is very near to it, any of those projections mentioned as suitable for Africa may be used. For a country rather more north or south, a suitable projection would be one of those suggested for China, etc.
Small Countries, except those on or near the Equator—e.g. Spain, Italy, Great Britain, Scandinavia, etc.	1. Equal-area.	Conical Equal-area with One Standard Parallel. Albers'. Bonne. As no particular advantage is gained by using a strictly equal-area projection for an atlas map of a small country, the two following projections are usually quite suitable:
	2. General.	Simple Conic with One Standard Parallel. Simple Conic with Two Standard Parallels.

Large-scale (Topographical) Maps.	Cassini's Projection by Rectangular Co-ordinates. The Modified Polyconic as used in the "One-in-a-Million" Map. The Rectangular Polyconic. [War Office Projection.] Modified Rectangular Polyconic. Airy's Zenithal Projection by Balance of Errors (as in the "Ten Miles to the Inch" Map of United Kingdom). Transverse Mercator [see pages 194–6].
Special Maps. 1. Navigation. 2. Air. 3. Directional Wireless. 4. Reverse Azimuths.	Mercator. [See also Close's Two-Point Equidistant Projection.] Mercator and possibly Gnomonic. Gnomonic; Maurer's Orthodromic or the Two-Point Azimuthal. Retro-Azimuthal Projections [see pages 196–8].

APPENDIX II

ELEMENTARY TRIGONOMETRY

THE non-mathematician, when first introduced to the study of map projections, often feels appalled at the sight of the mathematical symbols that occur in nearly all books on the subject. However, it is really surprising how little mathematical knowledge is required to render easy, not only the understanding, but also the construction of most of the projections in common use.

At the outset, let us consider why we need trigonometry at all. By derivation the word means "the measurement of triangles." In actual practice it is a means of linking up, as it were, the sides and angles of a triangle. There is no difficulty in measuring a line or an angle ; we want to go a step further : to find the lengths of the other sides and the size of other angles of a triangle about which we know, e.g. one side and two angles, or two sides and one angle, etc. Let us take a very simple example. A ladder leans against a vertical wall, and makes an angle of unknown size with the ground, which we will assume is horizontal. The distance of the foot of the ladder from the foot of the wall is 12 feet, and the ladder reaches a point 30 feet up the wall. At what angle does the ladder slope ? We know two facts—the distance of the ladder from the wall and the height of the top of the ladder above the ground.

Call the wall BC, the ladder AB, and the ground AC, as in fig. 86.

Suppose it were possible to shift the wall backwards and forwards so that it occupied the positions marked by the lines 1, 2, and 3, but at the same time NOT altering the slope (i.e. the angle of inclination which the ladder makes with the ground) of the ladder, but allowing it to grow longer or shorter as the case may be.

By doing this we have made several right-angled triangles, all of which have angles of the same value

ELEMENTARY TRIGONOMETRY

In each separate case the height of the ladder up the wall varies, and also the distance of the foot of the ladder from the foot of the wall, but the slope does not alter.

It will be seen from the figure that the angle BAC remains constant, wherever the wall may be. In other words, the ratio of the wall to the ground is a constant, and this ratio is called the tangent of the angle BAC.

We can measure the slope by means of a protractor if we plot the figure to scale. But this is rather clumsy and—as we shall soon see—very unnecessary.

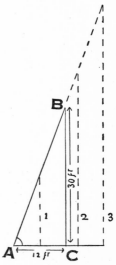

Instead of doing this, let us express the distance which the ladder extends up the wall and the distance of its foot from the wall as a ratio, and write it BC/AC. We know BC = 30 feet, and AC = 12 feet, or BC/AC = 2·5.

If we call this ratio the TANGENT of the angle BAC we have made use of trigonometry, and looking up in a table of tangents the value of 2·5 expressed in degrees, we shall find it is (approximately) 68° 12′ —in other words, the ladder makes an angle with the ground of 68° 12′.

FIG. 86.—Diagram illustrating Appendix IV.

If we wish to find the length of the ladder itself in the particular case when its foot is 12 feet from the wall, its top 30 feet up the wall, we can make use of another ratio, or we can find it by means of Pythagoras's Theorem : " That the square on the hypotenuse of a right-angled triangle is equal to the sum of the squares on the other two sides." We can put this in the following form :

$$AB^2 = AC^2 + BC^2$$
$$\text{and } AB = \sqrt{AC^2 + BC^2}$$
$$= \sqrt{12^2 + 30^2}$$
$$= 32\cdot 31 \text{ feet.}$$

207

If we made use of trigonometry, the SECANT of the angle BAC is AB/AC.

We know $\overline{\text{BAC}}$ = 68° 12′, and from tables we find the secant of this angle is 2·6927.

Therefore AB/AC = 2·6927
and as AC = 12 feet, AB = AC × 2·6927
= 12 feet × 2·6927 = 32·3124 feet.

We have now found the lengths of all the sides of the triangle and the value of the angle BAC. As we are dealing with a right-angled triangle, we know that the angle ABC = 90° − $\overline{\text{BAC}}$ = 90° − 68° 12′ = 21° 48′.

The triangle is now " solved," and simple trigonometry deals with the solution of triangles.

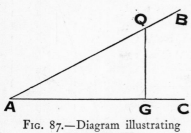

Fig. 87.—Diagram illustrating Appendix IV.

In introducing the tangent and the secant in this example we have anticipated somewhat, in order to show the need for, and the uses of, elementary trigonometry. The following lines will deal with the matter in a more logical sequence.

In the solution of right-angled triangles there are practically only three ratios to remember. In actual use there are six, but the second three are only the reciprocals of the first three.

Let BAC be an acute angle. Take any point G in AC and erect the perpendicular QG. Then, on any scale, measure AG and QG, and work out the ratio QG/AG to two or three places of decimals. Do the same when G is taken in another part of AC. The values of AG and QG will change, but the ratio QG/AG will not. This ratio QG/AG is called the tangent of the angle BAC (fig. 87).

Giving actual values, let us assume that the angle BAC = 30°, and AG = 2″. Then QG/AG = tangent of the angle BAC.

Therefore $QG = AG \times$ tangent $30°$
$$= 2 \times 0\text{·}5774$$
$$= 1''\text{·}1548.$$

The next two ratios are the sine and cosine. Using the same figure as before and drawing QG perpendicular to AC, work out the ratios QG/AQ and AG/AQ. Do the same thing after altering the position of QG. It will be found that the ratios QG/AQ and AG/AQ remain the same. The ratio QG/AQ is called the sine of the angle BAC, and the ratio AG/AQ is called the cosine of the angle BAC.

We may consider any right-angled triangle, and having one side and one angle given, we can find the other angles and sides —in other words, we can "solve" the triangle.

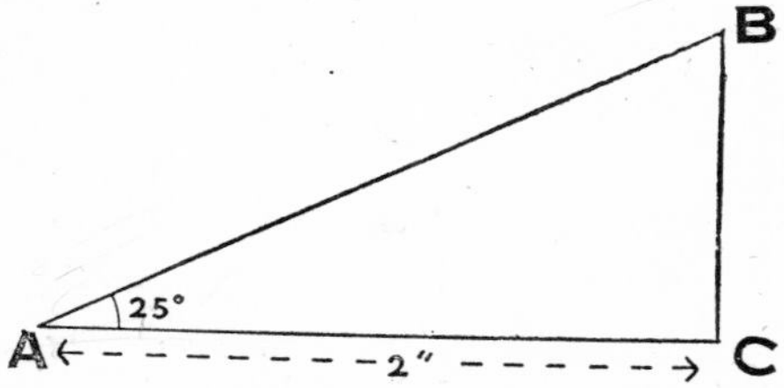

Let ABC be such a triangle with the right angle at C and angle BAC = 25°. AC = 2″ (fig. 88).

Fig. 88.—Diagram illustrating Appendix IV.

Now BC/AC = tangent of the angle BAC.

Therefore $BC = AC \times \tan 25°$
$$= 2 \times 0\text{·}4663$$
$$= 0''\text{·}9326.$$

Since the angle BAC = 25°, and angle BCA = 90°, the angle ABC = 90° − 25° = 65°.

We can now find the third side, AB, by means of geometry.

By Euclid I. 47; $AB^2 = AC^2 + BC^2$
$$= 2^2 + 0\text{·}9326^2$$
$$= 4\text{·}8697$$
and $AB = \sqrt{4\text{·}8697} = 2''\text{·}207.$

However, it is inconvenient to have to resort to squares and square roots. It is here that the next three ratios are useful.

In the triangle ABC we have :

1. BC/AC = tan /BAC.
2. BC/AB = sin /BAC.
3. AC/AB = cos /BAC.

In other words, tan /BAC = opposite side/adjacent side

sin /BAC = opposite side/hypotenuse

cos /BAC = adjacent side/hypotenuse.

The reciprocals of these three ratios are, respectively, the cotangent (cot), the cosecant (cosec), and the secant (sec) of the angle BAC.

Thus   cot /BAC = adjacent side/opposite side

cosec /BAC = hypotenuse/opposite side

sec /BAC = hypotenuse/adjacent side.

Any right-angled triangle can now be solved wholly by means of trigonometry.   In the triangle ABC (fig. 88) we have AC = 2″, /BAC = 25°, and /BCA = 90°.

Therefore /ABC = 65°

and we have seen that BC = AC tan /BAC = 0″·9326.

To find AB : By ratio AB/AC = sec /BAC

therefore AB = AC sec 25°

= 2 × 1·1034 = 2″·2068.

One further point may be noted.   So far reference has always been made to the angle BAC.   The solution could have been made just as easily by means of the angle ABC (= 90° − 25°).

In this case we have the following ratios, and if the reader wishes, it is quite easy to prove that they give the same results.

1. AC/BC = tan /ABC, and BC/AC = cot /ABC.
2. BC/AB = cos /ABC, and AB/BC = sec /ABC.
3. AC/AB = sin /ABC, and AB/AC = cosec /ABC.

In other words, the tangent (or sine or cosine) of the one angle is equal to the cotangent, etc., of its complement.

ELEMENTARY TRIGONOMETRY

Circular Measure

So far we have dealt with simple right-angled triangles. Let us now turn to another form of triangle—triangles in which one side is part of a circle and the other two sides radii. It is common knowledge that the diameter of any circle bears a certain proportion to the length of the circumference ; this proportion is called π, and its true value is $3{\cdot}14159265\ldots$, or approximately $3{\cdot}1416$ or $3\tfrac{1}{7}$.

If any part of the circumference of a circle is considered, and the ends of the arc are joined by straight lines (radii) to the centre of the circle, we have a triangle, one of whose sides is curved. Such a figure (AOB, fig. 89) is called a " sector " of a circle. It follows that as the length of the arc AB is increased or decreased, so does the value of the angle AOB increase or decrease—in fact, in the same circle arcs are proportional to the angles which they subtend at the centre.

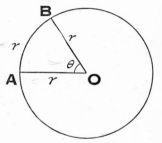

FIG. 89.—Diagram illustrating Appendix IV.

Now, if an arc be made of the same length as the radius of a circle, it subtends a constant angle at the centre. This constant angle is called a RADIAN, and the value of 1 radian in degrees is $57{\cdot}296$.

The proof of this is simple (fig. 89) :

O is the centre of a circle of radius r

Let arc AB $= r$.

Whole circumference $= 2\pi r$, but as AB $= r$, AB $= 1/2\pi$ of the whole circumference.

Further, as there are four right angles at the centre of any circle, the angle BOA $= 1/2\pi$ of 4 right angles

$$= 1/2\pi \text{ of } 360°$$
$$= \frac{1 \times 360°}{2 \times 3{\cdot}1416}$$
$$= 57°{\cdot}296.$$

211

APPENDIX II

In other words θ, the angle subtended at the centre, is constant, no matter how great r is.

Having found the value of a radian, we may define the circular measure of an angle—it is the number of radians which the angle contains.

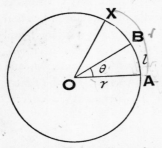

It has been shown that 1 radian
$$= (1/2\pi) \times 360°$$
$$= (1/\pi) \times 180°.$$

From this it follows that $1° = \pi/180$ radians, and also the special case: π radians $= 180°$, or 2 right angles.

Proceeding now to the more general aspect of the case, we have in fig. 90 the angle $BOA = \theta$ and the radius $OA = r$.

Call the arc BA, l.

FIG. 90.—Diagram illustrating Appendix IV.

It is required to prove that $l = r\theta$.

Suppose $\angle XOA = 1$ radian. Since 1 radian is subtended by an arc equal to the radius of the circle, $XA = r$.

Because arcs are proportional to the angles they subtend,

and $\angle BOA = \theta \times \angle XOA$

therefore arc $BA = \theta \times$ arc XA

or $l = r\theta$

whence it follows that $\theta = l/r$

and $r = l/\theta$.

Or, putting it another way, the circular measure of an angle subtended by an arc of the circumference at the centre of the circle is the ratio of the arc to the radius.

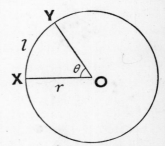

FIG. 91.—Diagram illustrating Appendix IV.

A few examples will make this matter clear

In fig. 91 let $r = 3''$, and $\theta = 30°$.

Then $l = r\theta$
$$= 3 \times 30° \text{ (in radians)}$$
$$= 3 \times 0·5236 = 1''·5708$$

212

In fig. 91 let arc $XY = 2''{\cdot}5$, and $r = 3''$.

Then $\theta = l/r = 2{\cdot}5/3 = 0{\cdot}8333 = 47°{\cdot}73$.

Finally, suppose (fig. 91) $\theta = 50°$, and $l = 4''$.

Then $r = l/\theta = 4/0{\cdot}8727 = 4''{\cdot}6$.

LOGARITHMS

	0	1	2	3	4	5	6	7	8	9	1	2	3	4	5	6	7	8	9
															Mean Differences.				
10	0000	0043	0086	0128	0170	0212	0253	0294	0334	0374	4	8	12	17	21	25	29	33	37
11	0414	0453	0492	0531	0569	0607	0645	0682	0719	0755	4	8	11	15	19	23	26	30	34
12	0792	0828	0864	0899	0934	0969	1004	1038	1072	1106	3	7	10	14	17	21	24	28	31
13	1139	1173	1206	1239	1271	1303	1335	1367	1399	1430	3	6	10	13	16	19	23	26	29
14	1461	1492	1523	1553	1584	1614	1644	1673	1703	1732	3	6	9	12	15	18	21	24	27
15	1761	1790	1818	1847	1875	1903	1931	1959	1987	2014	3	6	8	11	14	17	20	22	25
16	2041	2068	2095	2122	2148	2175	2201	2227	2253	2279	3	5	8	11	13	16	18	21	24
17	2304	2330	2355	2380	2405	2430	2455	2480	2504	2529	2	5	7	10	12	15	17	20	22
18	2553	2577	2601	2625	2648	2672	2695	2718	2742	2765	2	5	7	9	12	14	16	19	21
19	2788	2810	2833	2856	2878	2900	2923	2945	2967	2989	2	4	7	9	11	13	16	18	20
20	3010	3032	3054	3075	3096	3118	3139	3160	3181	3201	2	4	6	8	11	13	15	17	19
21	3222	3243	3263	3284	3304	3324	3345	3365	3385	3404	2	4	6	8	10	12	14	16	18
22	3424	3444	3464	3483	3502	3522	3541	3560	3579	3598	2	4	6	8	10	12	14	15	17
23	3617	3636	3655	3674	3692	3711	3729	3747	3766	3784	2	4	6	7	9	11	13	15	17
24	3802	3820	3838	3856	3874	3892	3909	3927	3945	3962	2	4	5	7	9	11	12	14	16
25	3979	3997	4014	4031	4048	4065	4082	4099	4116	4133	2	3	5	7	9	10	12	14	15
26	4150	4166	4183	4200	4216	4232	4249	4265	4281	4298	2	3	5	7	8	10	11	13	15
27	4314	4330	4346	4362	4378	4393	4409	4425	4440	4456	2	3	5	6	8	9	11	13	14
28	4472	4487	4502	4518	4533	4548	4564	4579	4594	4609	2	3	5	6	8	9	11	12	14
29	4624	4639	4654	4669	4683	4698	4713	4728	4742	4757	1	3	4	6	7	9	10	12	13
30	4771	4786	4800	4814	4829	4843	4857	4871	4886	4900	1	3	4	6	7	9	10	11	13
31	4914	4928	4942	4955	4969	4983	4997	5011	5024	5038	1	3	4	6	7	8	10	11	12
32	5051	5065	5079	5092	5105	5119	5132	5145	5159	5172	1	3	4	5	7	8	9	11	12
33	5185	5198	5211	5224	5237	5250	5263	5276	5289	5302	1	3	4	5	6	8	9	10	12
34	5315	5328	5340	5353	5366	5378	5391	5403	5416	5428	1	3	4	5	6	8	9	10	11
35	5441	5453	5465	5478	5490	5502	5514	5527	5539	5551	1	2	4	5	6	7	9	10	11
36	5563	5575	5587	5599	5611	5623	5635	5647	5658	5670	1	2	4	5	6	7	8	10	11
37	5682	5694	5705	5717	5729	5740	5752	5763	5775	5786	1	2	3	5	6	7	8	9	10
38	5798	5809	5821	5832	5843	5855	5866	5877	5888	5899	1	2	3	5	6	7	8	9	10
39	5911	5922	5933	5944	5955	5966	5977	5988	5999	6010	1	2	3	4	5	7	8	9	10
40	6021	6031	6042	6053	6064	6075	6085	6096	6107	6117	1	2	3	4	5	6	8	9	10
41	6128	6138	6149	6160	6170	6180	6191	6201	6212	6222	1	2	3	4	5	6	7	8	9
42	6232	6243	6253	6263	6274	6284	6294	6304	6314	6325	1	2	3	4	5	6	7	8	9
43	6335	6345	6355	6365	6375	6385	6395	6405	6415	6425	1	2	3	4	5	6	7	8	9
44	6435	6444	6454	6464	6474	6484	6493	6503	6513	6522	1	2	3	4	5	6	7	8	9
45	6532	6542	6551	6561	6571	6580	6590	6599	6609	6618	1	2	3	4	5	6	7	8	9
46	6628	6637	6646	6656	6665	6675	6684	6693	6702	6712	1	2	3	4	5	6	7	7	8
47	6721	6730	6739	6749	6758	6767	6776	6785	6794	6803	1	2	3	4	5	5	6	7	8
48	6812	6821	6830	6839	6848	6857	6866	6875	6884	6893	1	2	3	4	4	5	6	7	8
49	6902	6911	6920	6928	6937	6946	6955	6964	6972	6981	1	2	3	4	4	5	6	7	8
50	6990	6998	7007	7016	7024	7033	7042	7050	7059	7067	1	2	3	3	4	5	6	7	8
51	7076	7084	7093	7101	7110	7118	7126	7135	7143	7152	1	2	3	3	4	5	6	7	8
52	7160	7168	7177	7185	7193	7202	7210	7218	7226	7235	1	2	2	3	4	5	6	7	7
53	7243	7251	7259	7267	7275	7284	7292	7300	7308	7316	1	2	2	3	4	5	6	6	7
54	7324	7332	7340	7348	7356	7364	7372	7380	7388	7396	1	2	2	3	4	5	6	6	7
	0	1	2	3	4	5	6	7	8	9	1	2	3	4	5	6	7	8	9

LOGARITHMS

	0	1	2	3	4	5	6	7	8	9	Mean Differences.								
											1	2	3	4	5	6	7	8	9
55	7404	7412	7419	7427	7435	7443	7451	7459	7466	7474	1	2	2	3	4	5	5	6	7
56	7482	7490	7497	7505	7513	7520	7528	7536	7543	7551	1	2	2	3	4	5	5	6	7
57	7559	7566	7574	7582	7589	7597	7604	7612	7619	7627	1	2	2	3	4	5	5	6	7
58	7634	7642	7649	7657	7664	7672	7679	7686	7694	7701	1	1	2	3	4	4	5	6	7
59	7709	7716	7723	7731	7738	7745	7752	7760	7767	7774	1	1	2	3	4	4	5	6	7
60	7782	7789	7796	7803	7810	7818	7825	7832	7839	7846	1	1	2	3	4	4	5	6	6
61	7853	7860	7868	7875	7882	7889	7896	7903	7910	7917	1	1	2	3	4	4	5	6	6
62	7924	7931	7938	7945	7952	7959	7966	7973	7980	7987	1	1	2	3	3	4	5	6	6
63	7993	8000	8007	8014	8021	8028	8035	8041	8048	8055	1	1	2	3	3	4	5	5	6
64	8062	8069	8075	8082	8089	8096	8102	8109	8116	8122	1	1	2	3	3	4	5	5	6
65	8129	8136	8142	8149	8156	8162	8169	8176	8182	8189	1	1	2	2	3	4	5	5	6
66	8195	8202	8209	8215	8222	8228	8235	8241	8248	8254	1	1	2	3	3	4	5	5	6
67	8261	8267	8274	8280	8287	8293	8299	8306	8312	8319	1	1	2	3	3	4	5	5	6
68	8325	8331	8338	8344	8351	8357	8363	8370	8376	8382	1	1	2	3	3	4	4	5	6
69	8388	8395	8401	8407	8414	8420	8426	8432	8439	8445	1	1	2	2	3	4	4	5	6
70	8451	8457	8463	8470	8476	8482	8488	8494	8500	8506	1	1	2	2	3	4	4	5	6
71	8513	8519	8525	8531	8537	8543	8549	8555	8561	8567	1	1	2	2	3	4	4	5	5
72	8573	8579	8585	8591	8597	8603	8609	8615	8621	8627	1	1	2	2	3	4	4	5	5
73	8633	8639	8645	8651	8657	8663	8669	8675	8681	8686	1	1	2	2	3	4	4	5	5
74	8692	8698	8704	8710	8716	8722	8727	8733	8739	8745	1	1	2	2	3	4	4	5	5
75	8751	8756	8762	8768	8774	8779	8785	8791	8797	8802	1	1	2	2	3	3	4	5	5
76	8808	8814	8820	8825	8831	8837	8842	8848	8854	8859	1	1	2	2	3	3	4	5	5
77	8865	8871	8876	8882	8887	8893	8899	8904	8910	8915	1	1	2	2	3	3	4	4	5
78	8921	8927	8932	8938	8943	8949	8954	8960	8965	8971	1	1	2	2	3	3	4	4	5
79	8976	8982	8987	8993	8998	9004	9009	9015	9020	9025	1	1	2	2	3	3	4	4	5
80	9031	9036	9042	9047	9053	9058	9063	9069	9074	9079	1	1	2	2	3	3	4	4	5
81	9085	9090	9096	9101	9106	9112	9117	9122	9128	9133	1	1	2	2	3	3	4	4	5
82	9138	9143	9149	9154	9159	9165	9170	9175	9180	9186	1	1	2	2	3	3	4	4	5
83	9191	9196	9201	9206	9212	9217	9222	9227	9232	9238	1	1	2	2	3	3	4	4	5
84	9243	9248	9253	9258	9263	9269	9274	9279	9284	9289	1	1	2	2	3	3	4	4	5
85	9294	9299	9304	9309	9315	9320	9325	9330	9335	9340	1	1	2	2	3	3	4	4	5
86	9345	9350	9355	9360	9365	9370	9375	9380	9385	9390	1	1	2	2	3	3	4	4	5
87	9395	9400	9405	9410	9415	9420	9425	9430	9435	9440	0	1	1	2	2	3	3	4	4
88	9445	9450	9455	9460	9465	9469	9474	9479	9484	9489	0	1	1	2	2	3	3	4	4
89	9494	9499	9504	9509	9513	9518	9523	9528	9533	9538	0	1	1	2	2	3	3	4	4
90	9542	9547	9552	9557	9562	9566	9571	9576	9581	9586	0	1	1	2	2	3	3	4	4
91	9590	9595	9600	9605	9609	9614	9619	9624	9628	9633	0	1	1	2	2	3	3	4	4
92	9638	9643	9647	9652	9657	9661	9666	9671	9675	9680	0	1	1	2	2	3	3	4	4
93	9685	9689	9694	9699	9703	9708	9713	9717	9722	9727	0	1	1	2	2	3	3	4	4
94	9731	9736	9741	9745	9750	9754	9759	9763	9768	9773	0	1	1	2	2	3	3	4	4
95	9777	9782	9786	9791	9795	9800	9805	9809	9814	9818	0	1	1	2	2	3	3	4	4
96	9823	9827	9832	9836	9841	9845	9850	9854	9859	9863	0	1	1	2	2	3	3	4	4
97	9868	9872	9877	9881	9886	9890	9894	9899	9903	9908	0	1	1	2	2	3	3	4	4
98	9912	9917	9921	9926	9930	9934	9939	9943	9948	9952	0	1	1	2	2	3	3	4	4
99	9956	9961	9965	9969	9974	9978	9983	9987	9991	9996	0	1	1	2	2	3	3	3	4
	0	1	2	3	4	5	6	7	8	9	1	2	3	4	5	6	7	8	9

ANTILOGARITHMS

	0	1	2	3	4	5	6	7	8	9	1	2	3	4	5	6	7	8	9
															Mean Differences.				
·00	1000	1002	1005	1007	1009	1012	1014	1016	1019	1021	0	0	1	1	1	1	2	2	2
·01	1023	1026	1028	1030	1033	1035	1038	1040	1042	1045	0	0	1	1	1	1	2	2	2
·02	1047	1050	1052	1054	1057	1059	1062	1064	1067	1069	0	0	1	1	1	1	2	2	2
·03	1072	1074	1076	1079	1081	1084	1086	1089	1091	1094	0	0	1	1	1	1	2	2	2
·04	1096	1099	1102	1104	1107	1109	1112	1114	1117	1119	0	1	1	1	1	2	2	2	2
·05	1122	1125	1127	1130	1132	1135	1138	1140	1143	1146	0	1	1	1	1	2	2	2	2
·06	1148	1151	1153	1156	1159	1161	1164	1167	1169	1172	0	1	1	1	1	2	2	2	2
·07	1175	1178	1180	1183	1186	1189	1191	1194	1197	1199	0	1	1	1	1	2	2	2	2
·08	1202	1205	1208	1211	1213	1216	1219	1222	1225	1227	0	1	1	1	1	2	2	2	3
·09	1230	1233	1236	1239	1242	1245	1247	1250	1253	1256	0	1	1	1	1	2	2	2	3
·10	1259	1262	1265	1268	1271	1274	1276	1279	1282	1285	0	1	1	1	1	2	2	2	3
·11	1288	1291	1294	1297	1300	1303	1306	1309	1312	1315	0	1	1	1	2	2	2	2	3
·12	1318	1321	1324	1327	1330	1334	1337	1340	1343	1346	0	1	1	1	2	2	2	2	3
·13	1349	1352	1355	1358	1361	1365	1368	1371	1374	1377	0	1	1	1	2	2	2	3	3
·14	1380	1384	1387	1390	1393	1396	1400	1403	1406	1409	0	1	1	1	2	2	2	3	3
·15	1413	1416	1419	1422	1426	1429	1432	1435	1439	1442	0	1	1	1	2	2	2	3	3
·16	1445	1449	1452	1455	1459	1462	1466	1469	1472	1476	0	1	1	1	2	2	2	3	3
·17	1479	1483	1486	1489	1493	1496	1500	1503	1507	1510	0	1	1	1	2	2	2	3	3
·18	1514	1517	1521	1524	1528	1531	1535	1538	1542	1545	0	1	1	1	2	2	2	3	3
·19	1549	1552	1556	1560	1563	1567	1570	1574	1578	1581	0	1	1	1	2	2	3	3	3
·20	1585	1589	1592	1596	1600	1603	1607	1611	1614	1618	0	1	1	1	2	2	3	3	3
·21	1622	1626	1629	1633	1637	1641	1644	1648	1652	1656	0	1	1	2	2	2	3	3	3
·22	1660	1663	1667	1671	1675	1679	1683	1687	1690	1694	0	1	1	2	2	2	3	3	3
·23	1698	1702	1706	1710	1714	1718	1722	1726	1730	1734	0	1	1	2	2	2	3	3	4
·24	1738	1742	1746	1750	1754	1758	1762	1766	1770	1774	0	1	1	2	2	2	3	3	4
·25	1778	1782	1786	1791	1795	1799	1803	1807	1811	1816	0	1	1	2	2	2	3	3	4
·26	1820	1824	1828	1832	1837	1841	1845	1849	1854	1858	0	1	1	2	2	3	3	3	4
·27	1862	1866	1871	1875	1879	1884	1888	1892	1897	1901	0	1	1	2	2	3	3	3	4
·28	1905	1910	1914	1919	1923	1928	1932	1936	1941	1945	0	1	1	2	2	3	3	4	4
·29	1950	1954	1959	1963	1968	1972	1977	1982	1986	1991	0	1	1	2	2	3	3	4	4
·30	1995	2000	2004	2009	2014	2018	2023	2028	2032	2037	0	1	1	2	2	3	3	4	4
·31	2042	2046	2051	2056	2061	2065	2070	2075	2080	2084	0	1	1	2	2	3	3	4	4
·32	2089	2094	2099	2104	2109	2113	2118	2123	2128	2133	0	1	1	2	2	3	3	4	4
·33	2138	2143	2148	2153	2158	2163	2168	2173	2178	2183	0	1	1	2	2	3	3	4	4
·34	2188	2193	2198	2203	2208	2213	2218	2223	2228	2234	1	1	2	2	3	3	4	4	5
·35	2239	2244	2249	2254	2259	2265	2270	2275	2280	2286	1	1	2	2	3	3	4	4	5
·36	2291	2296	2301	2307	2312	2317	2323	2328	2333	2339	1	1	2	2	3	3	4	4	5
·37	2344	2350	2355	2360	2366	2371	2377	2382	2388	2393	1	1	2	2	3	3	4	4	5
·38	2399	2404	2410	2415	2421	2427	2432	2438	2443	2449	1	1	2	2	3	3	4	4	5
·39	2455	2460	2466	2472	2477	2483	2489	2495	2500	2506	1	1	2	2	3	3	4	5	5
·40	2512	2518	2523	2529	2535	2541	2547	2553	2559	2564	1	1	2	2	3	4	4	5	5
·41	2570	2576	2582	2588	2594	2600	2606	2612	2618	2624	1	1	2	2	3	4	4	5	5
·42	2630	2636	2642	2649	2655	2661	2667	2673	2679	2685	1	1	2	2	3	4	4	5	6
·43	2692	2698	2704	2710	2716	2723	2729	2735	2742	2748	1	1	2	3	3	4	4	5	6
·44	2754	2761	2767	2773	2780	2786	2793	2799	2805	2812	1	1	2	3	3	4	4	5	6
·45	2818	2825	2831	2838	2844	2851	2858	2864	2871	2877	1	1	2	3	3	4	5	5	6
·46	2884	2891	2897	2904	2911	2917	2924	2931	2938	2944	1	1	2	3	3	4	5	5	6
·47	2951	2958	2965	2972	2979	2985	2992	2999	3006	3013	1	1	2	3	3	4	5	5	6
·48	3020	3027	3034	3041	3048	3055	3062	3069	3076	3083	1	1	2	3	4	4	5	6	6
·49	3090	3097	3105	3112	3119	3126	3133	3141	3148	3155	1	1	2	3	4	4	5	6	6

ANTILOGARITHMS

	0	1	2	3	4	5	6	7	8	9	1	2	3	4	5	6	7	8	9
															Mean Differences.				
·50	3162	3170	3177	3184	3192	3199	3206	3214	3221	3228	1	1	2	3	4	4	5	6	7
·51	3236	3243	3251	3258	3266	3273	3281	3289	3296	3304	1	2	2	3	4	5	5	6	7
·52	3311	3319	3327	3334	3342	3350	3357	3365	3373	3381	1	2	2	3	4	5	5	6	7
·53	3388	3396	3404	3412	3420	3428	3436	3443	3451	3459	1	2	2	3	4	5	6	6	7
·54	3467	3475	3483	3491	3499	3508	3516	3524	3532	3540	1	2	2	3	4	5	6	6	7
·55	3548	3556	3565	3573	3581	3589	3597	3606	3614	3622	1	2	2	3	4	5	6	7	7
·56	3631	3639	3648	3656	3664	3673	3681	3690	3698	3707	1	2	3	3	4	5	6	7	8
·57	3715	3724	3733	3741	3750	3758	3767	3776	3784	3793	1	2	3	3	4	5	6	7	8
·58	3802	3811	3819	3828	3837	3846	3855	3864	3873	3882	1	2	3	4	4	5	6	7	8
·59	3890	3899	3908	3917	3926	3936	3945	3954	3963	3972	1	2	3	4	5	5	6	7	8
·60	3981	3990	3999	4009	4018	4027	4036	4046	4055	4064	1	2	3	4	5	6	6	7	8
·61	4074	4083	4093	4102	4111	4121	4130	4140	4150	4159	1	2	3	4	5	6	7	8	9
·62	4169	4178	4188	4198	4207	4217	4227	4236	4246	4256	1	2	3	4	5	6	7	8	9
·63	4266	4276	4285	4295	4305	4315	4325	4335	4345	4355	1	2	3	4	5	6	7	8	9
·64	4365	4375	4385	4395	4406	4416	4426	4436	4446	4457	1	2	3	4	5	6	7	8	9
·65	4467	4477	4487	4498	4508	4519	4529	4539	4550	4560	1	2	3	4	5	6	7	8	9
·66	4571	4581	4592	4603	4613	4624	4634	4645	4656	4667	1	2	3	4	5	6	7	9	10
·67	4677	4688	4699	4710	4721	4732	4742	4753	4764	4775	1	2	3	4	5	7	8	9	10
·68	4786	4797	4808	4819	4831	4842	4853	4864	4875	4887	1	2	3	4	6	7	8	9	10
·69	4898	4909	4920	4932	4943	4955	4966	4977	4989	5000	1	2	3	5	6	7	8	9	10
·70	5012	5023	5035	5047	5058	5070	5082	5093	5105	5117	1	2	4	5	6	7	8	9	11
·71	5129	5140	5152	5164	5176	5188	5200	5212	5224	5236	1	2	4	5	6	7	8	10	11
·72	5248	5260	5272	5284	5297	5309	5321	5333	5346	5358	1	2	4	5	6	7	9	10	11
·73	5370	5383	5395	5408	5420	5433	5445	5458	5470	5483	1	3	4	5	6	8	9	10	11
·74	5495	5508	5521	5534	5546	5559	5572	5585	5598	5610	1	3	4	5	6	8	9	10	12
·75	5623	5636	5649	5662	5675	5689	5702	5715	5728	5741	1	3	4	5	7	8	9	10	12
·76	5754	5768	5781	5794	5808	5821	5834	5848	5861	5875	1	3	4	5	7	8	9	11	12
·77	5888	5902	5916	5929	5943	5957	5970	5984	5998	6012	1	3	4	5	7	8	10	11	12
·78	6026	6039	6053	6067	6081	6095	6109	6124	6138	6152	1	3	4	6	7	8	10	11	13
·79	6166	6180	6194	6209	6223	6237	6252	6266	6281	6295	1	3	4	6	7	9	10	11	13
·80	6310	6324	6339	6353	6368	6383	6397	6412	6427	6442	1	3	4	6	7	9	10	12	13
·81	6457	6471	6486	6501	6516	6531	6546	6561	6577	6592	2	3	5	6	8	9	11	12	14
·82	6607	6622	6637	6653	6668	6683	6699	6714	6730	6745	2	3	5	6	8	9	11	12	14
·83	6761	6776	6792	6808	6823	6839	6855	6871	6887	6902	2	3	5	6	8	9	11	13	14
·84	6918	6934	6950	6966	6982	6998	7015	7031	7047	7063	2	3	5	6	8	10	11	13	15
·85	7079	7096	7112	7129	7145	7161	7178	7194	7211	7228	2	3	5	7	8	10	12	13	15
·86	7244	7261	7278	7295	7311	7328	7345	7362	7379	7396	2	3	5	7	8	10	12	13	15
·87	7413	7430	7447	7464	7482	7499	7516	7534	7551	7568	2	3	5	7	9	10	12	14	16
·88	7586	7603	7621	7638	7656	7674	7691	7709	7727	7745	2	4	5	7	9	11	12	14	16
·89	7762	7780	7798	7816	7834	7852	7870	7889	7907	7925	2	4	5	7	9	11	13	14	16
·90	7943	7962	7980	7998	8017	8035	8054	8072	8091	8110	2	4	6	7	9	11	13	15	17
·91	8128	8147	8166	8185	8204	8222	8241	8260	8279	8299	2	4	6	8	9	11	13	15	17
·92	8318	8337	8356	8375	8395	8414	8433	8453	8472	8492	2	4	6	8	10	12	14	15	17
·93	8511	8531	8551	8570	8590	8610	8630	8650	8670	8690	2	4	6	8	10	12	14	16	18
·94	8710	8730	8750	8770	8790	8810	8831	8851	8872	8892	2	4	6	8	10	12	14	16	18
·95	8913	8933	8954	8974	8995	9016	9036	9057	9078	9099	2	4	6	8	10	12	15	17	19
·96	9120	9141	9162	9183	9204	9226	9247	9268	9290	9311	2	4	6	8	11	13	15	17	19
·97	9333	9354	9376	9397	9419	9441	9462	9484	9506	9528	2	4	7	9	11	13	15	17	20
·98	9550	9572	9594	9616	9638	9661	9683	9705	9727	9750	2	4	7	9	11	13	16	18	20
·99	9772	9795	9817	9840	9863	9886	9908	9931	9954	9977	2	5	7	9	11	14	16	18	20

Angle.	Log. Sines.	Log. Cosines.	Log. Tangents.	Log. Cotangents.	Log. Secants.	Log. Cosecants.
0°	$-\infty$	0·0000	$-\infty$	$+\infty$	0·0000	$+\infty$
1	$\bar{2}$·2419	$\bar{1}$·9999	$\bar{2}$·2419	1·7581	0·0001	1·7581
2	$\bar{2}$·5428	$\bar{1}$·9997	$\bar{2}$·5431	1·4569	0·0003	1·4572
3	$\bar{2}$·7188	$\bar{1}$·9994	$\bar{2}$·7194	1·2806	0·0006	1·2812
4	$\bar{2}$·8436	$\bar{1}$·9989	$\bar{2}$·8446	1·1554	0·0011	1·1564
5	$\bar{2}$·9403	$\bar{1}$·9983	$\bar{2}$·9420	1·0580	0·0017	1·0597
6	$\bar{1}$·0192	$\bar{1}$·9976	$\bar{1}$·0216	0·9784	0·0024	0·9808
7	$\bar{1}$·0859	$\bar{1}$·9968	$\bar{1}$·0891	0·9109	0·0032	0·9141
8	$\bar{1}$·1436	$\bar{1}$·9958	$\bar{1}$·1478	0·8522	0·0042	0·8564
9	$\bar{1}$·1943	$\bar{1}$·9946	$\bar{1}$·1997	0·8003	0·0054	0·8057
10	$\bar{1}$·2397	$\bar{1}$·9934	$\bar{1}$·2463	0·7537	0·0066	0·7603
11	$\bar{1}$·2806	$\bar{1}$·9919	$\bar{1}$·2887	0·7113	0·0081	0·7194
12	$\bar{1}$·3179	$\bar{1}$·9904	$\bar{1}$·3275	0·6725	0·0096	0·6821
13	$\bar{1}$·3521	$\bar{1}$·9887	$\bar{1}$·3634	0·6366	0·0113	0·6479
14	$\bar{1}$·3837	$\bar{1}$·9869	$\bar{1}$·3968	0·6032	0·0131	0·6163
15	$\bar{1}$·4130	$\bar{1}$·9849	$\bar{1}$·4281	0·5719	0·0151	0·5870
16	$\bar{1}$·4403	$\bar{1}$·9828	$\bar{1}$·4575	0·5425	0·0172	0·5597
17	$\bar{1}$·4659	$\bar{1}$·9806	$\bar{1}$·4853	0·5147	0·0194	0·5341
18	$\bar{1}$·4900	$\bar{1}$·9782	$\bar{1}$·5118	0·4882	0·0218	0·5100
19	$\bar{1}$·5126	$\bar{1}$·9757	$\bar{1}$·5370	0·4630	0·0243	0·4874
20	$\bar{1}$·5341	$\bar{1}$·9730	$\bar{1}$·5611	0·4389	0·0270	0·4659
21	$\bar{1}$·5543	$\bar{1}$·9702	$\bar{1}$·5842	0·4158	0·0298	0·4457
22	$\bar{1}$·5736	$\bar{1}$·9672	$\bar{1}$·6064	0·3936	0·0328	0·4264
23	$\bar{1}$·5919	$\bar{1}$·9640	$\bar{1}$·6279	0·3721	0·0360	0·4081
24	$\bar{1}$·6093	$\bar{1}$·9607	$\bar{1}$·6486	0·3514	0·0393	0·3907
25	$\bar{1}$·6259	$\bar{1}$·9573	$\bar{1}$·6687	0·3313	0·0427	0·3741
26	$\bar{1}$·6418	$\bar{1}$·9537	$\bar{1}$·6882	0·3118	0·0463	0·3582
27	$\bar{1}$·6570	$\bar{1}$·9499	$\bar{1}$·7072	0·2928	0·0501	0·3430
28	$\bar{1}$·6716	$\bar{1}$·9459	$\bar{1}$·7257	0·2743	0·0541	0·3284
29	$\bar{1}$·6856	$\bar{1}$·9418	$\bar{1}$·7438	0·2562	0·0582	0·3144
30	$\bar{1}$·6990	$\bar{1}$·9375	$\bar{1}$·7614	0·2386	0·0625	0·3010
31	$\bar{1}$·7118	$\bar{1}$·9331	$\bar{1}$·7788	0·2212	0·0669	0·2882
32	$\bar{1}$·7242	$\bar{1}$·9284	$\bar{1}$·7958	0·2042	0·0716	0·2758
33	$\bar{1}$·7361	$\bar{1}$·9236	$\bar{1}$·8125	0·1875	0·0764	0·2639
34	$\bar{1}$·7476	$\bar{1}$·9186	$\bar{1}$·8290	0·1710	0·0814	0·2524
35	$\bar{1}$·7586	$\bar{1}$·9134	$\bar{1}$·8452	0·1548	0·0866	0·2414
36	$\bar{1}$·7692	$\bar{1}$·9080	$\bar{1}$·8613	0·1387	0·0920	0·2308
37	$\bar{1}$·7795	$\bar{1}$·9023	$\bar{1}$·8771	0·1229	0·0977	0·2205
38	$\bar{1}$·7893	$\bar{1}$·8965	$\bar{1}$·8928	0·1072	0·1035	0·2107
39	$\bar{1}$·7989	$\bar{1}$·8905	$\bar{1}$·9084	0·0916	0·1095	0·2011
40	$\bar{1}$·8081	$\bar{1}$·8843	$\bar{1}$·9238	0·0762	0·1157	0·1919
41	$\bar{1}$·8169	$\bar{1}$·8778	$\bar{1}$·9392	0·0608	0·1222	0·1831
42	$\bar{1}$·8255	$\bar{1}$·8711	$\bar{1}$·9544	0·0456	0·1289	0·1745
43	$\bar{1}$·8338	$\bar{1}$·8641	$\bar{1}$·9697	0·0303	0·1359	0·1662
44	$\bar{1}$·8418	$\bar{1}$·8569	$\bar{1}$·9848	0·0152	0·1431	0·1582

Angle.	Log. Sines.	Log. Cosines.	Log. Tangents.	Log. Cotangents.	Log. Secants.	Log. Cosecants.
45°	$\overline{1}$·8495	$\overline{1}$·8495	0·0000	0·0000	0·1505	0·1505
46	$\overline{1}$·8569	$\overline{1}$·8418	0·0152	$\overline{1}$·9848	0·1582	0·1431
47	$\overline{1}$·8641	$\overline{1}$·8338	0·0303	$\overline{1}$·9697	0·1662	0·1359
48	$\overline{1}$·8711	$\overline{1}$·8255	0·0456	$\overline{1}$·9544	0·1745	0·1289
49	$\overline{1}$·8778	$\overline{1}$·8169	0·0608	$\overline{1}$·9392	0·1831	0·1222
50	$\overline{1}$·8843	$\overline{1}$·8081	0·0762	$\overline{1}$·9238	0·1919	0·1157
51	$\overline{1}$·8905	$\overline{1}$·7989	0·0916	$\overline{1}$·9084	0·2011	0·1095
52	$\overline{1}$·8965	$\overline{1}$·7893	0·1072	$\overline{1}$·8928	0·2107	0·1035
53	$\overline{1}$·9023	$\overline{1}$·7795	0·1229	$\overline{1}$·8771	0·2205	0·0977
54	$\overline{1}$·9080	$\overline{1}$·7692	0·1387	$\overline{1}$·8613	0·2308	0·0920
55	$\overline{1}$·9134	$\overline{1}$·7586	0·1548	$\overline{1}$·8452	0·2414	0·0866
56	$\overline{1}$·9186	$\overline{1}$·7476	0·1710	$\overline{1}$·8290	0·2524	0·0814
57	$\overline{1}$·9236	$\overline{1}$·7361	0·1875	$\overline{1}$·8125	0·2639	0·0764
58	$\overline{1}$·9284	$\overline{1}$·7242	0·2042	$\overline{1}$·7958	0·2758	0·0716
59	$\overline{1}$·9331	$\overline{1}$·7118	0·2212	$\overline{1}$·7788	0·2882	0·0669
60	$\overline{1}$·9375	$\overline{1}$·6990	0·2386	$\overline{1}$·7614	0·3010	0·0625
61	$\overline{1}$·9418	$\overline{1}$·6856	0·2562	$\overline{1}$·7438	0·3144	0·0582
62	$\overline{1}$·9459	$\overline{1}$·6716	0·2743	$\overline{1}$·7257	0·3284	0·0541
63	$\overline{1}$·9499	$\overline{1}$·6570	0·2928	$\overline{1}$·7072	0·3430	0·0501
64	$\overline{1}$·9537	$\overline{1}$·6418	0·3118	$\overline{1}$·6882	0·3582	0·0463
65	$\overline{1}$·9573	$\overline{1}$·6259	0·3313	$\overline{1}$·6687	0·3741	0·0427
66	$\overline{1}$·9607	$\overline{1}$·6093	0·3514	$\overline{1}$·6486	0·3907	0·0393
67	$\overline{1}$·9640	$\overline{1}$·5919	0·3721	$\overline{1}$·6279	0·4081	0·0360
68	$\overline{1}$·9672	$\overline{1}$·5736	0·3936	$\overline{1}$·6064	0·4264	0·0328
69	$\overline{1}$·9702	$\overline{1}$·5543	0·4158	$\overline{1}$·5842	0·4457	0·0298
70	$\overline{1}$·9730	$\overline{1}$·5341	0·4389	$\overline{1}$·5611	0·4659	0·0270
71	$\overline{1}$·9757	$\overline{1}$·5126	0·4630	$\overline{1}$·5370	0·4874	0·0243
72	$\overline{1}$·9782	$\overline{1}$·4900	0·4882	$\overline{1}$·5118	0·5100	0·0218
73	$\overline{1}$·9806	$\overline{1}$·4659	0·5147	$\overline{1}$·4853	0·5341	0·0194
74	$\overline{1}$·9828	$\overline{1}$·4403	0·5425	$\overline{1}$·4575	0·5597	0·0172
75	$\overline{1}$·9849	$\overline{1}$·4130	0·5719	$\overline{1}$·4281	0·5870	0·0151
76	$\overline{1}$·9869	$\overline{1}$·3837	0·6032	$\overline{1}$·3968	0·6163	0·0131
77	$\overline{1}$·9887	$\overline{1}$·3521	0·6366	$\overline{1}$·3634	0·6479	0·0113
78	$\overline{1}$·9904	$\overline{1}$·3179	0·6725	$\overline{1}$·3275	0·6821	0·0096
79	$\overline{1}$·9919	$\overline{1}$·2806	0·7113	$\overline{1}$·2887	0·7194	0·0081
80	$\overline{1}$·9934	$\overline{1}$·2397	0·7537	$\overline{1}$·2463	0·7603	0·0066
81	$\overline{1}$·9946	$\overline{1}$·1943	0·8003	$\overline{1}$·1997	0·8057	0·0054
82	$\overline{1}$·9958	$\overline{1}$·1436	0·8522	$\overline{1}$·1478	0·8564	0·0042
83	$\overline{1}$·9968	$\overline{1}$·0859	0·9109	$\overline{1}$·0891	0·9141	0·0032
84	$\overline{1}$·9976	$\overline{1}$·0192	0·9784	$\overline{1}$·0216	0·9808	0·0024
85	$\overline{1}$·9983	$\overline{2}$·9403	1·0580	$\overline{2}$·9420	1·0597	0·0017
86	$\overline{1}$·9989	$\overline{2}$·8436	1·1554	$\overline{2}$·8446	1·1564	0·0011
87	$\overline{1}$·9994	$\overline{2}$·7188	1·2806	$\overline{2}$·7194	1·2812	0·0006
88	$\overline{1}$·9997	$\overline{2}$·5428	1·4569	$\overline{2}$·5431	1·4572	0·0003
89	$\overline{1}$·9999	$\overline{2}$·242	1·758	$\overline{2}$·242	1·7581	0·0001

Angle.	Nat. Sines.	Nat. Cosines.	Nat. Tangents.	Nat. Cotangents.	Nat. Secants.	Nat. Cosecants.
0°	·0000	1·0000	0·0000	∞	1·0000	∞
1	·0175	·9998	0·0175	57·29	1·0002	57·30
2	·0349	·9994	0·0349	28·64	1·0006	28·65
3	·0523	·9986	0·0524	19·08	1·0014	19·11
4	·0698	·9976	0·0699	14·30	1·0024	14·34
5	·0872	·9962	0·0875	11·43	1·0038	11·47
6	·1045	·9945	0·1051	9·514	1·0055	9·567
7	·1219	·9925	0·1228	8·144	1·0075	8·206
8	·1392	·9903	0·1405	7·115	1·0098	7·185
9	·1564	·9877	0·1584	6·314	1·0125	6·392
10	·1736	·9848	0·1763	5·6713	1·0154	5·7588
11	·1908	·9816	0·1944	5·1446	1·0187	5·2408
12	·2079	·9781	0·2126	4·7046	1·0223	4·8097
13	·2250	·9744	0·2309	4·3315	1·0263	4·4454
14	·2419	·9703	0·2493	4·0108	1·0306	4·1336
15	·2588	·9659	0·2679	3·7321	1·0353	3·8637
16	·2756	·9613	0·2867	3·4874	1·0403	3·6280
17	·2924	·9563	0·3057	3·2709	1·0457	3·4203
18	·3090	·9511	0·3249	3·0777	1·0515	3·2361
19	·3256	·9455	0·3443	2·9042	1·0576	3·0716
20	·3420	·9397	0·3640	2·7475	1·0642	2·9238
21	·3584	·9336	0·3839	2·6051	1·0711	2·7904
22	·3746	·9272	0·4040	2·4751	1·0785	2·6695
23	·3907	·9205	0·4245	2·3559	1·0864	2·5593
24	·4067	·9135	0·4452	2·2460	1·0946	2·4586
25	·4226	·9063	0·4663	2·1445	1·1034	2·3662
26	·4384	·8988	0·4877	2·0503	1·1126	2·2812
27	·4540	·8910	0·5095	1·9626	1·1223	2·2027
28	·4695	·8829	0·5317	1·8807	1·1326	2·1301
29	·4848	·8746	0·5543	1·8040	1·1434	2·0627
30	·5000	·8660	0·5774	1·7321	1·1547	2·0000
31	·5150	·8572	0·6009	1·6643	1·1666	1·9416
32	·5299	·8480	0·6249	1·6003	1·1792	1·8871
33	·5446	·8387	0·6494	1·5399	1·1924	1·8361
34	·5592	·8290	0·6745	1·4826	1·2062	1·7883
35	·5736	·8192	0·7002	1·4281	1·2208	1·7434
36	·5878	·8090	0·7265	1·3764	1·2361	1·7013
37	·6018	·7986	0·7536	1·3270	1·2521	1·6616
38	·6157	·7880	0·7813	1·2799	1·2690	1·6243
39	·6293	·7771	0·8098	1·2349	1·2868	1·5890
40	·6428	·7660	0·8391	1·1918	1·3054	1·5557
41	·6561	·7547	0·8693	1·1504	1·3250	1·5243
42	·6691	·7431	0·9004	1·1106	1·3456	1·4945
43	·6820	·7314	0·9325	1·0724	1·3673	1·4663
44	·6947	·7193	0·9657	1·0355	1·3902	1·4396

Angle.	Nat. Sines.	Nat. Cosines.	Nat. Tangents.	Nat. Cotangents.	Nat. Secants.	Nat. Cosecants.
45	·7071	·7071	1·0000	1·0000	1·4142	1·4142
46	·7193	·6947	1·0355	0·9657	1·4396	1·3902
47	·7314	·6820	1·0724	0·9325	1·4663	1·3673
48	·7431	·6691	1·1106	0·9004	1·4945	1·3456
49	·7547	·6561	1·1504	0·8693	1·5243	1·3250
50	·7660	·6428	1·1918	0·8391	1·5557	1·3054
51	·7771	·6293	1·2349	0·8098	1·5890	1·2868
52	·7880	·6157	1·2799	0·7813	1·6243	1·2690
53	·7986	·6018	1·3270	0·7536	1·6616	1·2521
54	·8090	·5878	1·3764	0·7265	1·7013	1·2361
55	·8192	·5736	1·4281	0·7002	1·7434	1·2208
56	·8290	·5592	1·4826	0·6745	1·7883	1·2062
57	·8387	·5446	1·5399	0·6494	1·8361	1·1924
58	·8480	·5299	1·6003	0·6249	1·8871	1·1792
59	·8572	·5150	1·6643	0·6009	1·9416	1·1666
60	·8660	·5000	1·7321	0·5774	2·0000	1·1547
61	·8746	·4848	1·8040	0·5543	2·0627	1·1434
62	·8829	·4695	1·8807	0·5317	2·1301	1·1326
63	·8910	·4540	1·9626	0·5095	2·2027	1·1223
64	·8988	·4384	2·0503	0·4877	2·2812	1·1126
65	·9063	·4226	2·1445	0·4663	2·3662	1·1034
66	·9135	·4067	2·2460	0·4452	2·4586	1·0946
67	·9205	·3907	2·3559	0·4245	2·5593	1·0864
68	·9272	·3746	2·4751	0·4040	2·6695	1·0785
69	·9336	·3584	2·6051	0·3839	2·7904	1·0711
70	·9397	·3420	2·7475	0·3640	2·9238	1·0642
71	·9455	·3256	2·9042	0·3443	3·0716	1·0576
72	·9511	·3090	3·0777	0·3249	3·2361	1·0515
73	·9563	·2924	3·2709	0·3057	3·4203	1·0457
74	·9613	·2756	3·4874	0·2867	3·6280	1·0403
75	·9659	·2588	3·7321	0·2679	3·8637	1·0353
76	·9703	·2419	4·0108	0·2493	4·1336	1·0306
77	·9744	·2250	4·3315	0·2309	4·4454	1·0263
78	·9781	·2079	4·7046	0·2126	4·8097	1·0223
79	·9816	·1908	5·1446	0·1944	5·2408	1·0187
80	·9848	·1736	5·671	0·1763	5·759	1·0154
81	·9877	·1564	6·314	0·1584	6·392	1·0125
82	·9903	·1392	7·115	0·1405	7·185	1·0098
83	·9925	·1219	8·144	0·1228	8·206	1·0075
84	·9945	·1045	9·51	0·1051	9·57	1·0055
85	·9962	·0872	11·43	0·0875	11·47	1·0038
86	·9976	·0698	14·30	0·0699	14·34	1·0024
87	·9986	·0523	19·08	0·0524	19·11	1·0014
88	·9994	·0349	28·64	0·0349	28·65	1·0006
89	·9998	·0175	57·29	0·0175	57·30	1·0002

°	Rad.	°	Rad.	°	Rad.	'	Rad.	'	Rad.
0	0·0000	30	0·5236	60	1·0472	0	·0000	30	·0087
1	0·0175	31	0·5411	61	1·0647	1	·0003	31	·0090
2	0·0349	32	0·5585	62	1·0821	2	·0006	32	·0093
3	0·0524	33	0·5760	63	1·0996	3	·0009	33	·0096
4	0·0698	34	0·5934	64	1·1170	4	·0012	34	·0099
5	0·0873	35	0·6109	65	1·1345	5	·0015	35	·0102
6	0·1047	36	0·6283	66	1·1519	6	·0017	36	·0105
7	0·1222	37	0·6458	67	1·1694	7	·0020	37	·0108
8	0·1396	38	0·6632	68	1·1868	8	·0023	38	·0111
9	0·1571	39	0·6807	69	1·2043	9	·0026	39	·0113
10	0·1745	40	0·6981	70	1·2217	10	·0029	40	·0116
11	0·1920	41	0·7156	71	1·2392	11	·0032	41	·0119
12	0·2094	42	0·7330	72	1·2566	12	·0035	42	·0122
13	0·2269	43	0·7505	73	1·2741	13	·0038	43	·0125
14	0·2443	44	0·7679	74	1·2915	14	·0041	44	·0128
15	0·2618	45	0·7854	75	1·3090	15	·0044	45	·0131
16	0·2793	46	0·8029	76	1·3265	16	·0047	46	·0134
17	0·2967	47	0·8203	77	1·3439	17	·0049	47	·0137
18	0·3142	48	0·8378	78	1·3614	18	·0052	48	·0140
19	0·3316	49	0·8552	79	1·3788	19	·0055	49	·0143
20	0·3491	50	0·8727	80	1·3963	20	·0058	50	·0145
21	0·3665	51	0·8901	81	1·4137	21	·0061	51	·0148
22	0·3840	52	0·9076	82	1·4312	22	·0064	52	·0151
23	0·4014	53	0·9250	83	1·4486	23	·0067	53	·0154
24	0·4189	54	0·9425	84	1·4661	24	·0070	54	·0157
25	0·4363	55	0·9599	85	1·4835	25	·0073	55	·0160
26	0·4538	56	0·9774	86	1·5010	26	·0076	56	·0163
27	0·4712	57	0·9948	87	1·5184	27	·0079	57	·0166
28	0·4887	58	1·0123	88	1·5359	28	·0081	58	·0169
29	0·5061	59	1·0297	89	1·5533	29	·0084	59	·0172
30	0·5236	60	1·0472	90	1·5708	30	·0087	60	·0175

Rad.	Degrees
0·001	0·06
0·002	0·11
0·003	0·17
0·004	0·23
0·005	0·29
0·006	0·34
0·007	0·40
0·008	0·46
0·009	0·52
0·01	0·57
0·02	1·15
0·03	1·72
0·04	2·29
0·05	2·86
0·06	3·44
0·07	4·01
0·08	4·58
0·09	5·16
0·1	5·73
0·2	11·46
0·3	17·19
0·4	22·92
0·5	28·65
0·6	34·38
0·7	40·11
0·8	45·84
0·9	51·57
1	57·30
2	114·59
3	171·89
4	229·18
5	286·48
6	343·77

INDEX

INDEX

INDEX